Mastercam® X⁷
TRAINING GUIDE
LATHE

By Matthew Manton and Duane Weidinger

camInstructor

Mastercam® X7 Training Guide Lathe
Published by
CamInstructor Inc.
330 Chandos Crt.
Kitchener, Ontario
N2A 3C2
www.caminstructor.com

Date: March 1, 2013
Author: Matthew Manton and Duane Weidinger
ISBN: 978-1-927359-28-0

National Library of Canada Cataloguing in Publication

To order additional copies of the book contact CamInstructor at:

Canadian Office	Phone 1-877-873-6867
330 Chandos Crt	Fax 1-866-741-8421
Kitchener, ON	email sales@caminstructor.com
N2A 3C2	

Requirements
Use of this book requires Mastercam X7 Lathe. Use of the Multi-media CD/DVD requires a computer with speakers and a CD ROM.
April 5, 2013

How To Use The Training Guides

This book set includes 1 book and 1 CD/DVD;
1. Mastercam Training Guide for Lathe
2. Mastercam Training Multi-media instruction for Lathe

The software required to use this book is as follows:
- o Mastercam X7 Lathe

Use of the Multi-media CD/DVD requires a computer with speakers and a CD/DVD ROM.

Both the book and CD/DVD are meant to be used in conjunction with each other, for example Lesson 1 in the Mastercam Training Guide relates to Lesson 1 in on the CD/DVD.

Each Lesson has all the information required to create the Geometry, Toolpaths and G-Code (NC code) for the part.

Lesson 1 is the easiest Lesson to complete. Each Lesson gets progressively more detailed, therefore it is important for new users to start with Lesson 1 and progress through each Lesson in order.

We recommend the following as a guideline;

Mastercam Experience	Lessons
No Mastercam Experience	Start with Lesson 1 and then complete 2, 3, 4, 5, 6, 7, 8 and 9 in that order.
Experience using V8 or V9 Lathe	Start with Lesson 1, then jump to Lesson 3 then complete 4, 5, 6, 7, 8 and 9
Experience using any previous VX Lathe	Start with Lesson 4, then complete 5, 6, 7, 8 and 9.

All the Lessons in this book are designed to be machined using 6061 Aluminum. In most cases the parts are machined from standard 1.5 inch diameter stock.

Material Size and required Cutters for each Lesson is listed in the Setup Sheet at the beginning of each Lesson.

If you have any suggestions on how this Training Guide can be improved please email duane.weidinger@caminstructor.com.

Contents at a Glance

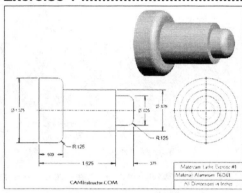

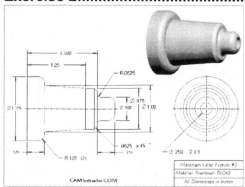

Lathe

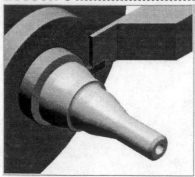

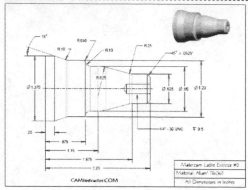

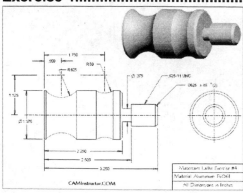

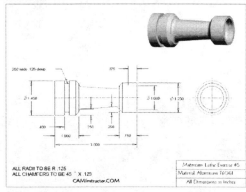

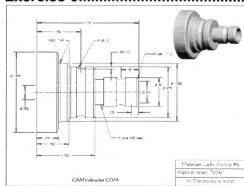

Lathe

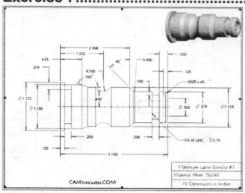

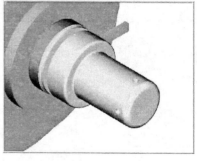

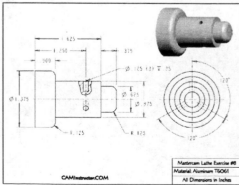

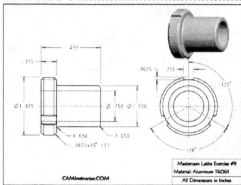

What's on the CD/DVD?

1. Training Videos
Getting Started-Video
- An overview of how the CD/DVD works

Setting the Mastercam Environment

Tips and Techniques-Videos
- Getting Help – 6 Minutes
- Lathe Diameter & Radius – 7 Minutes
- Creating Lines – 12 Minutes
- Creating Arcs and Circles – 12 Minutes
- Trim and Extend – 5 Minutes
- Xform – 9 Minutes
- Stock Setup – 8 Minutes
- Backplot and Verify – 5 Minutes

Lesson-1 through Lesson-9 Videos
- Video instructions on how to complete each Lesson from start to finish.

Mastercam-Files
- Mastercam files required by certain Lessons in the book

Mastercam HLE Installation Software
Install it onto your computer so you can practice and work in Mastercam. **Please note**; Mastercam HLE Software is a full working copy of Mastercam, however it will NOT allow you to create NC code.

Mastercam. X⁷

TRAINING

GUIDE

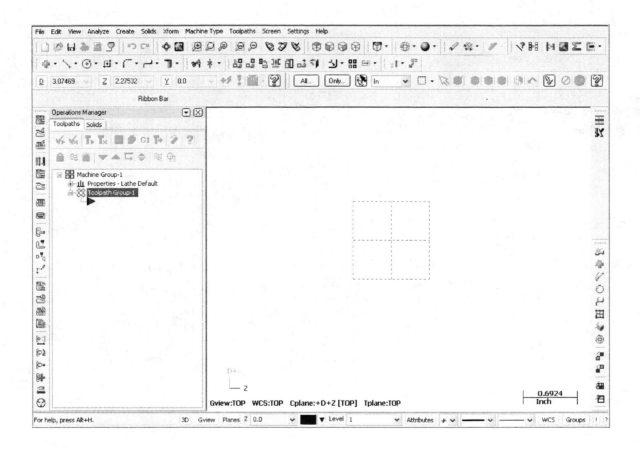

LATHE

SETTING THE ENVIRONMENT

camInstructor

SETTING THE ENVIRONMENT
COMPLETE THESE STEPS BEFORE STARTING EACH MODULE

Before starting the geometry creation and generating the toolpaths you should:

- ➲ Set the Grid. This will help identify the location of the origin.
- ➲ Customize the toolbars to machine a lathe part.
- ➲ Set the machine type to Lathe Default.

SETTING THE GRID:
1. Launch **Mastercam**.
2. Select from the pull down menu **Settings>Configuration**.

3. From the **Topics** window on the left side of this window expand the **Screen** topic by selecting the **+ sign** and then select **Grid Settings**.
4. Enable the **Visible Grid** and change the **Size to 1**.

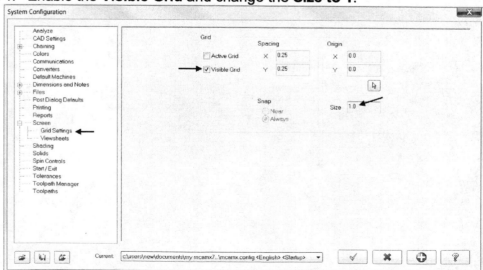

5. Select the **OK** button  to complete this function.

SETTING THE TOOLBARS FOR GEOMETRY CREATION AND MACHINING A LATHE PART:

1. Select from the pull down menu **Settings>Toolbar States**.
2. Select Lathe.
3. Then select the **Load** button.

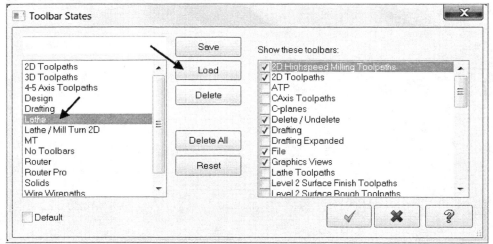

4. Select the **OK** button 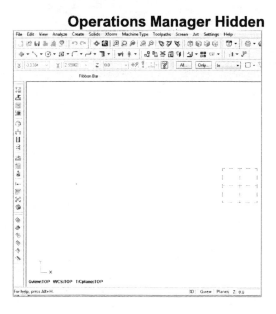 to accept the settings.

DISPLAYING THE OPERATIONS MANAGER:

1. To Show or Hide the **Operations Manager** pane on the left of the screen press **Alt + O**. Pressing **Alt + O** acts like a toggle switch between **Hide and Display**. For more information on the **Operations Manager** see the **Tips and Techniques** section on the **Multimedia CD** supplied with this text.

Operations Manager Hidden   **Operations Manager Displayed**

SELECTING THE TYPE OF MACHINE:
- ➲ For Lathe-Lessons 1 though 7 you will use the **Default Lathe** to machine the part.
- ➲ For Lathe-Lessons 8 and 9 you will use the **C-AXIS SLANT BED Lathe** to machine the part.

1. Select from the pull down menu **Machine Type>Lathe**.
2. Click on **Default** as shown below:

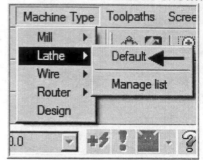

3. Your screen should look like the image shown below:

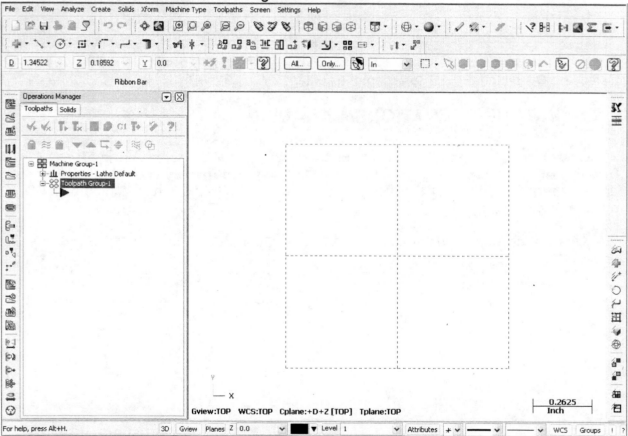

Mastercam® X⁷

TRAINING
GUIDE

LATHE-LESSON-1

FACE, ROUGH, FINISH AND CUTOFF

camInstructor

Objectives

You will create the geometry for Lathe-Lesson-1, and then generate a toolpath to machine the part on a CNC lathe. This lesson covers the following topics:

➲ **Create a 2-dimensional drawing by:**
Creating lines.
Creating fillets.

➲ **Establish Stock and Chuck settings:**
Stock size.
Chuck Configuration.
Material for the part.
Feed calculation.

➲ **Generate a 2-dimensional lathe toolpath consisting of:**
Lathe Face.
Lathe Rough.
Lathe Finish.
Lathe Cutoff.

➲ **Inspect the toolpath using Mastercam's Verify and Backplot by:**
Launching the Verify function to machine the part on the screen.
Using Backplot to identify the correctness of the toolpaths.
Generating the NC- code.

LATHE-LESSON-1 DRAWING

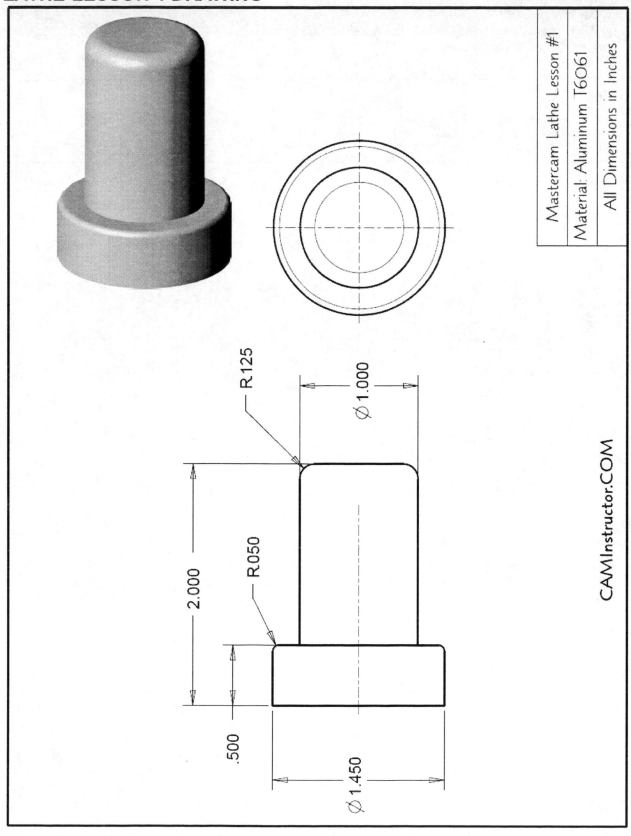

Mastercam Lathe Lesson #1

Material: Aluminum T6061

All Dimensions in Inches

CAMInstructor.COM

R125

Ø 1.000

R050

2.000

.500

Ø 1.450

TOOL LIST

Two tools will be used to create this part.
- ➲ Tool #1 Face, Rough and Finish the outside diameters
- ➲ Tool #2 Cutoff the part

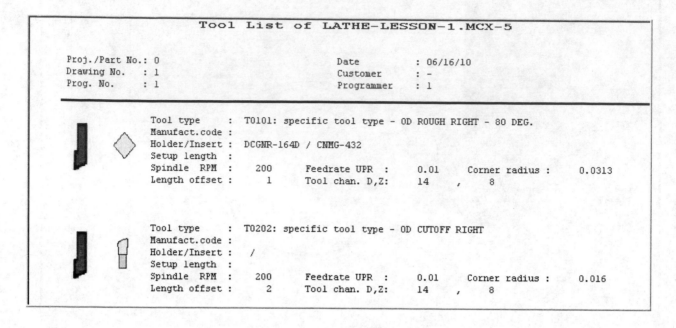

```
            Tool List of LATHE-LESSON-1.MCX-5

Proj./Part No.: 0                    Date       : 06/16/10
Drawing No.   : 1                    Customer   : -
Prog. No.     : 1                    Programmer : 1


         Tool type      : T0101: specific tool type - OD ROUGH RIGHT - 80 DEG.
         Manufact.code  :
         Holder/Insert  : DCGNR-164D / CNMG-432
         Setup length   :
         Spindle RPM  :     200    Feedrate UPR :   0.01    Corner radius :    0.0313
         Length offset :      1    Tool chan. D,Z:   14    ,     8


         Tool type      : T0202: specific tool type - OD CUTOFF RIGHT
         Manufact.code  :
         Holder/Insert  :   /
         Setup length   :
         Spindle RPM  :     200    Feedrate UPR :   0.01    Corner radius :    0.016
         Length offset :      2    Tool chan. D,Z:   14    ,     8
```

LATHE - LESSON - 1 - THE PROCESS

Geometry Creation

TASK 1:   Setting the Environment
TASK 2:   Setting the Construction Planes
TASK 3:   Create the Geometry
TASK 4:   Create the Fillets (Radius)
TASK 5:   Save the Drawing

Toolpath Creation

TASK 6:   Define the Stock and Chuck Parameters
TASK 7:   Face the Front of the Part
TASK 8:   Rough the Outside Diameters
TASK 9:   Finish the Outside Diameters
TASK 10:   Cut off the Part
TASK 11:   Backplot the Toolpath
TASK 12:   Verify the Toolpath
TASK 13:   Save the Updated Mastercam File
TASK 14:   Post and Create the CNC Code File

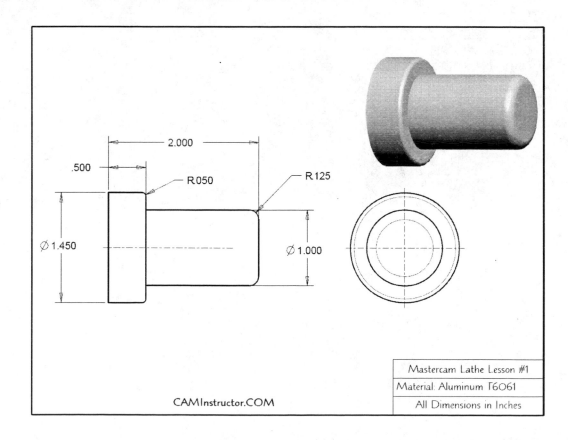

2.000

.500

R050

R125

Ø1.450

Ø1.000

CAMInstructor.COM

| Mastercam Lathe Lesson #1 |
| Material: Aluminum T6061 |
| All Dimensions in Inches |

Geometry Creation

TASK 1:
SETTING THE ENVIRONMENT

Before starting the geometry creation you should set up the grid and toolbars as outlined in the **Setting the Environment** section at the beginning of this text:
1. Set up the Grid. This will help identify the location of the origin.
2. Customize the toolbars to machine a part on the Lathe.
3. Set the machine type to the Lathe Default.

TASK 2:
SETTING THE CONSTRUCTION PLANES:

➲ **Set the Construction Plane to Lathe diameter +D +Z (WCS)**
1. Click on Planes at the bottom of the screen as shown below:

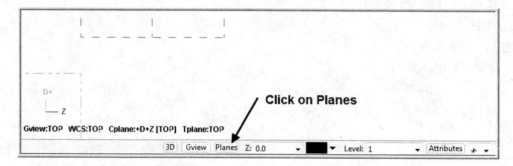

2. Click on Lathe diameter>+D +Z (WCS) as shown below:

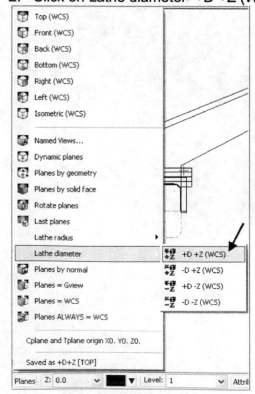

TASK 3:
CREATE THE GEOMETRY – THE RIGHT HAND FACE IS AT Z0

➲ This task explains how to create the geometry of this part. In this lathe part you only need to create **half of the geometry**, the geometry above the center line.

➲ Lines 1 through 5 will be created first and then the fillet and chamfer will be created.

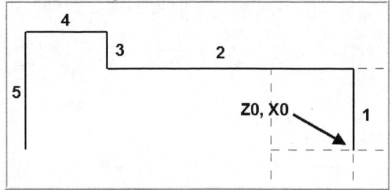

➲ **Create Line #1**

1. Watch the videos **Lesson-1 - Introduction** and **Lesson-1 - Task 1 to 3**.
2. Select from the pull down menu **Create>Line>Endpoint...**

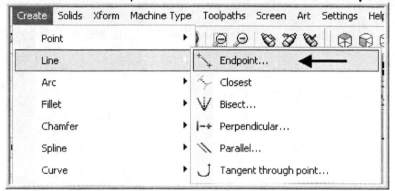

3. The **Line ribbon bar** appears.

4.   Move the cursor over the **center of the grid** and as you get close to the origin a visual cue appears. With this visual cue highlighted click the **left mouse** button.

➲ The following are Mastercam Visual Cues:

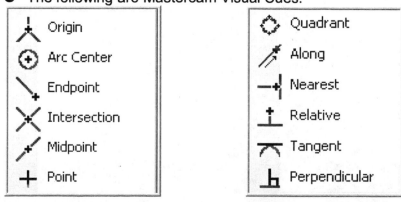

5. You are prompted to **"Specify the second endpoint"**. Click in the **D** value space (Diameter) (as shown by the arrow below) and enter a value of **1.0**. Hit the Enter key and enter a value of **0 for the Z**, hit the Enter key again and enter a value of **0 for the Y** enter.

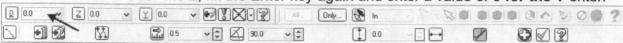

6. Click on Apply 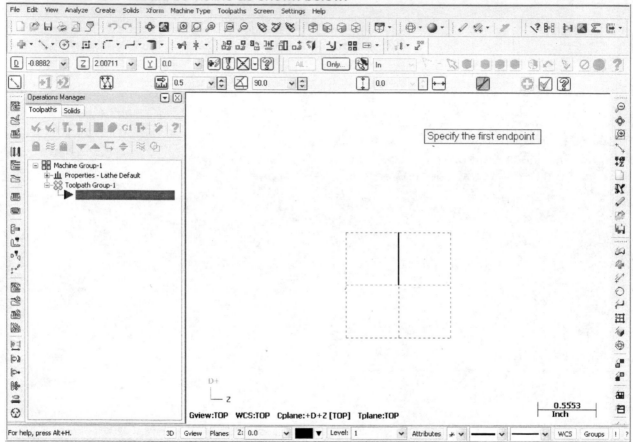.
7. A **vertical line** should be visible as shown below:

Specify the first endpoint

0.5553
Inch

Gview:TOP   WCS:TOP   Cplane:+D+Z [TOP]   Tplane:TOP

NOTE: If you make a mistake creating lines, click on the **Accept** icon ⊕ and click on the **Undo** icon. Then redo the Line.

➲ **Create Line #2.**

8. You are next prompted to **"Specify the first endpoint"**. Click on the **end of the line** that was just created as shown below and as you get close to the end point a visual cue appears. 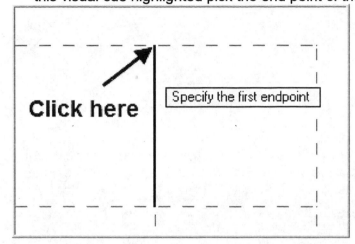 This is the cue that will allow you to snap to the endpoint of this line. With this visual cue highlighted pick the end point of the line.

Click here / Specify the first endpoint

9. You are next prompted to **"Specify the second endpoint"**. On the Line ribbon bar click in the **D** value space and enter **1.0**. Hit the Enter key and enter a value of **-1.5 for the Z**, hit the Enter key again and enter a value of **0 for the Y**. Hit the Enter key once again to complete this line.

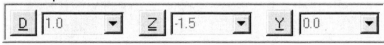

10. Click on Accept ⊕.

➲ **Create Line #3**

11. You are next prompted to **"Specify the first endpoint"**. Click on the **end of the line** that was just created as shown below:

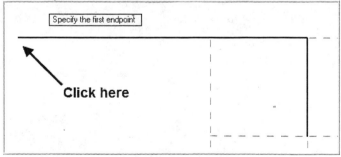
Specify the first endpoint / Click here

12. You are next prompted to **"Specify the second endpoint"**. On the Line ribbon bar click in the **D** value space (Diameter) and enter a value of **1.45**. Hit the Enter key and enter a value of **-1.5 for the Z**, hit the Enter key again and enter a value of **0 for the Y**. Hit the Enter key once again to complete this line.

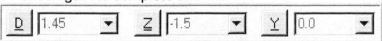

13. Click on Accept ⊕.

⊃ Create Line #4

14. You are next prompted to **"Specify the first endpoint"**. Click on the **end of the line** that was just created as shown below:

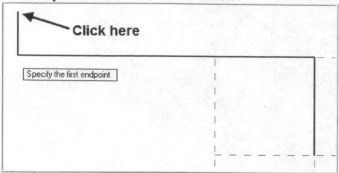

15. You are next prompted to **"Specify the second endpoint"**. On the Line ribbon bar click in the **D** value space (Diameter) and enter a value of **1.45**. Hit the Enter key and enter a value of **-2.0 for the Z**, hit the Enter key again and enter a value of **0 for the Y**. Hit the Enter key once again to complete this line.

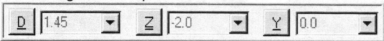

16. Click on **Accept** ⊕.

17. Fit the image to the screen by clicking on the **Fit to Screen** icon as shown below:

18. Then by clicking on the **Un-Zoom .8** icon as shown below:

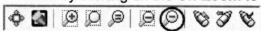

⊃ **Create Line #5**

19. You are next prompted to **"Specify the first endpoint"**. Click on the **end of the line** that was just created as shown below:

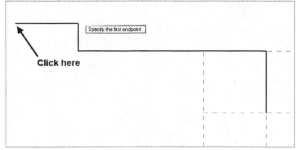

20. You are next prompted to **"Specify the second endpoint"**. On the Line ribbon bar click in the **D** value space (Diameter) and enter a value of **0**. Hit the Enter key and enter a value of **-2.0 for the Z**, hit the Enter key again and enter a value of **0 for the Y**. Hit the Enter key once again to complete this line.

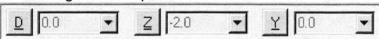

21. Click on the **OK** icon [✓] to complete this feature.

22. Select the **Screen Fit** icon to fit the part to the screen ⊕.

23. Your geometry should look like the figure below:

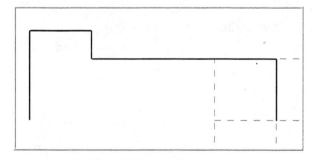

TASK 4:
CREATE THE FILLETS

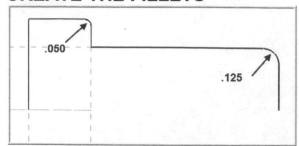

⊃ **Create the .050 fillet radius.**

1. Select **Create>Fillet>Entities…**

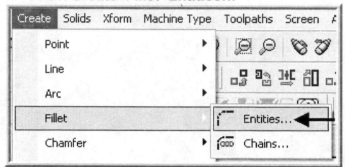

2. The **Fillet Entities** ribbon bar appears and you are prompted to **"Fillet: Select an entity"**.

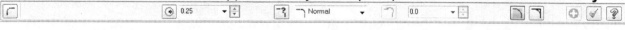

3. Click in the space for radius and input **.050** and then hit the tab key.

4. You are now transported over to the **Fillet Style field**. Click on the drop down arrow to review the various fillet radius styles and then ensure **Normal** is selected before moving on.

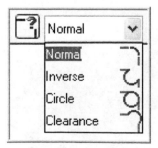

5. Ensure the **Trim** option for fillet is activated, the icon is depressed as shown below:

6. Click on **line 1** and then click on **Line 2** as shown below:

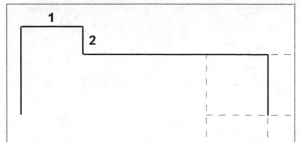

7. Click on the **OK** icon to complete this feature.

8. The completed fillet is shown below:

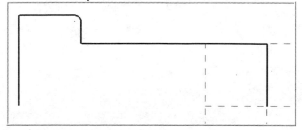

➲ **Create the .125 radius**

9. Select **Create>Fillet>Entities...**

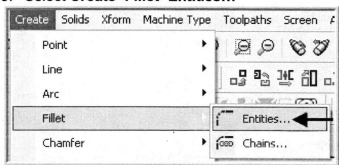

10. The **Fillet Entities** ribbon bar appears and you are prompted to **"Fillet: Select an entity"**.

11. Click in the space for radius and input **.125** and then hit the tab key.

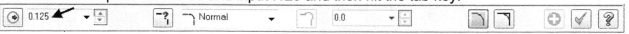

12. You are now transported over to the **Fillet Style field**. Ensure **Normal** is selected before moving on.

13. Ensure the **Trim** option for fillet is activated, the icon is depressed as shown below:

14. Click on **Line 1** and then click on **Line 2** as shown below:

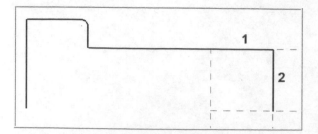

15. Click on the **OK** icon ☑ to complete this feature.

16. The completed fillet is shown below:

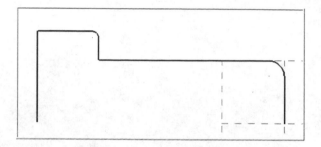

17. This completes the geometry for this part.

TASK 5:
SAVE THE DRAWING

1. Select **File.**
2. Select **Save As...**
3. In the **"File name"** box, type **Lathe-Lesson-1.**
4. Save to an appropriate location.
5. Select the Save button to save the file and complete this function.

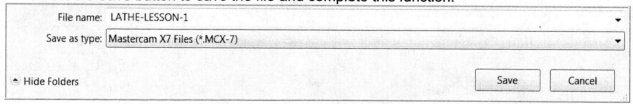

Toolpath Creation

TASK 6:
DEFINING THE STOCK AND CHUCK PARAMETERS

1. Select the **screen fit** icon  .

2. Select **Un Zoom previous / .5**  .
3. Ensure your screen looks like the image below:
   a. The Toolpaths Manager is open, if it is not Select Alt and O on your keyboard to open it.
   b. The properties icon displays Lathe Default. If it is not turn to the section titled **Setting the Environment** at the beginning of this book.
   c. The **Lathe - Lesson-1** Geometry is showing.

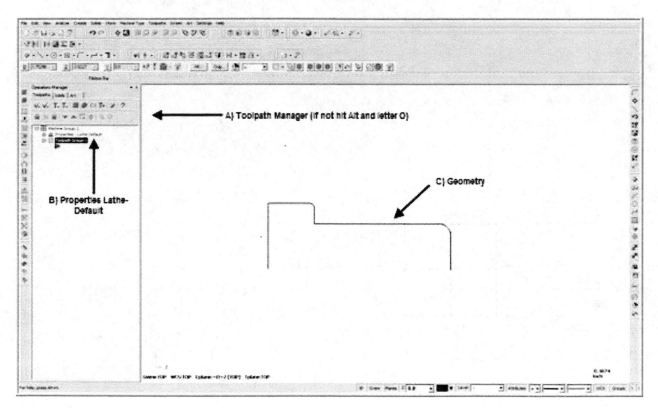

4. Select the plus in front of **Properties** to expand the Machine Group Properties.

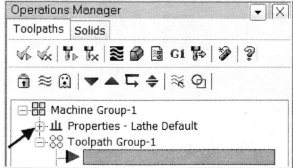

5. **This is optional** - To expand the toolpaths manager window, click on the outside of the window with the left mouse button (hold the button down) and drag it to the right.

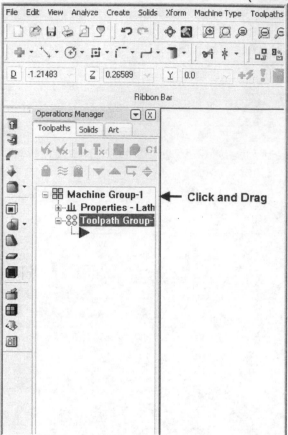

6. Select **Stock setup** in the Toolpaths Manager window.

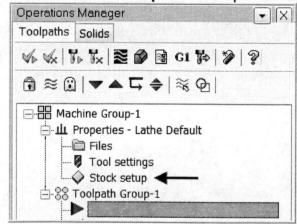

7. Select the **Stock Properties** button in the Stock Setup page as shown in the screenshot below:

➲ Note: To learn how to complete this section of the **Stock Setup** refer to the **Tips and Techniques** section on the Mastercam Training Guide – Lathe DVD that accompanies this book.

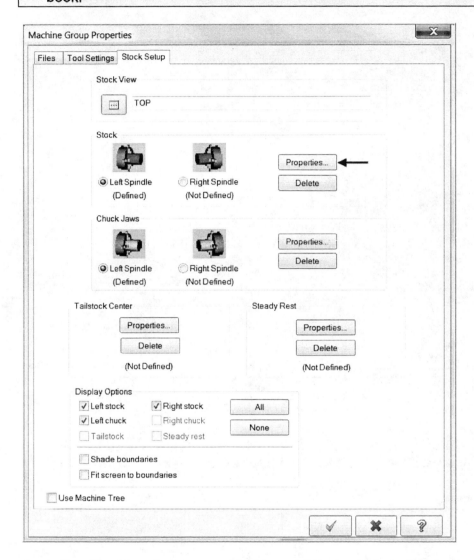

8. In the **Machine Component Manager-Stock** window click on the Geometry button and select Cylinder as shown below:

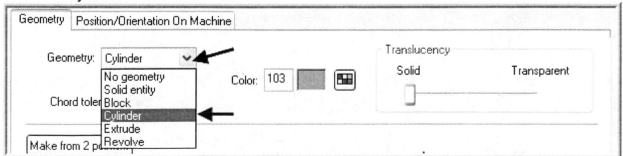

9. In the **Stock** setup set the values as shown below:

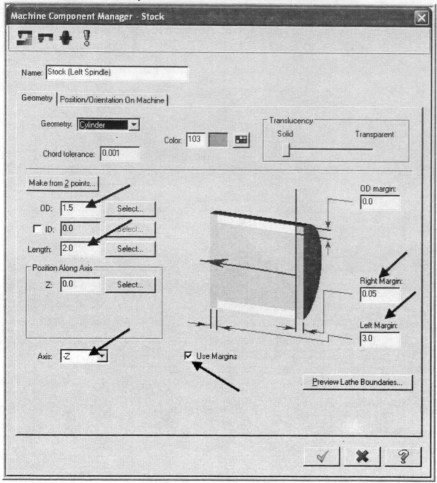

10. Click on the **OK** icon ☑ to complete this feature.
11. Select the **Chuck Properties** button in the Stock Setup page as shown in the screenshot below:

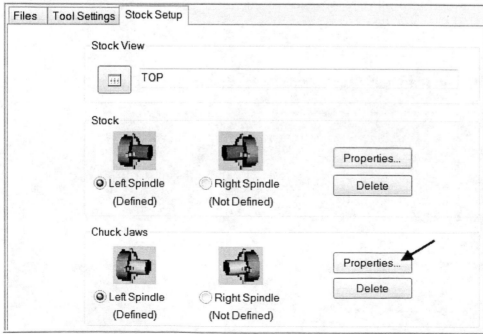

12. In the **Chuck Jaws** setup set the values as shown below:

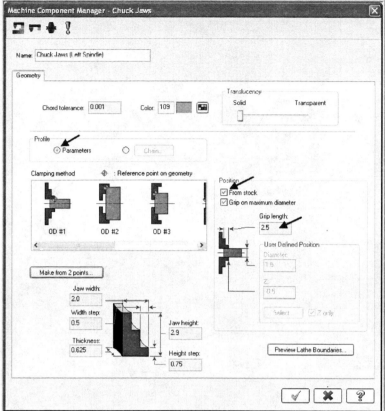

13. Click on the **OK** icon 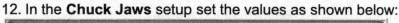 to complete this feature.
14. Click on the **Tool Settings** page:

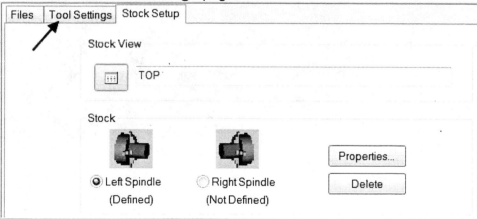

15. Make changes as shown below then click on the Select button:

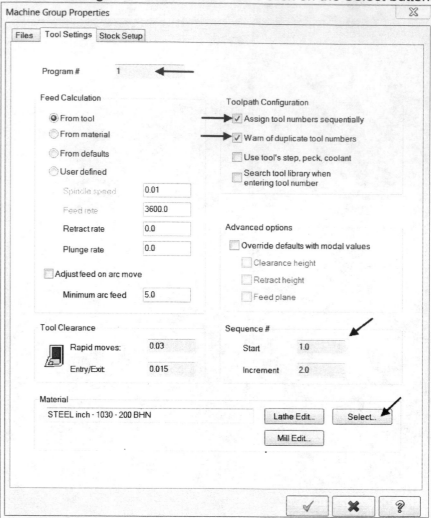

16. Select **Lathe – library** from the drop down **Material List** dialog box as shown below:

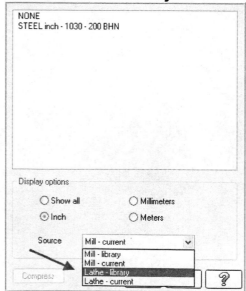

17. Select ALUMINIUM inch - 6061 from the Default Materials list.

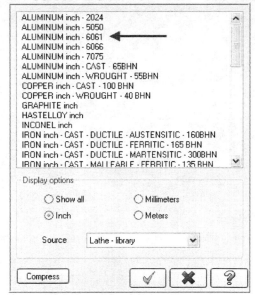

18. Select the OK button ✓.

19. Select the OK button ✓ again to complete this Stock Setup function.

20. Zoom out by clicking on the **Un-Zoom Previous** .5 icon

 Notice the stock setup outline as indicated by broken lines as shown below: (Note, you may have to click the **unzoom** button a number of times to see the entire image.)

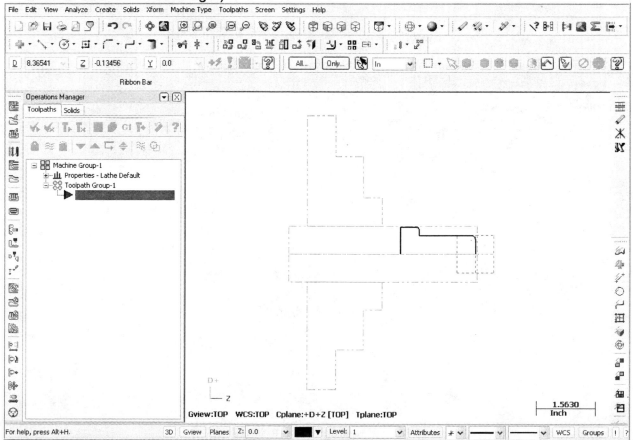

TASK 7:
FACE THE FRONT OF THE PART:
➾ In this task you will use a facing tool to face the front of the part in one cut.

1. Select the **Fit** icon as shown:

2. Then click on the **Un-Zoom .8** icon as shown below:

3. From the menu bar select **Toolpaths>Face...**

4. When prompted to **"Enter new NC name"** select the OK button ☑ to accept LATHE-LESSON-1 as shown below:

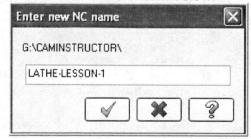

➲ After selecting the OK button you are confronted with **Toolpath parameters** page. The first task here will be to select **Tool #1 an OD Rough- Right – 80 deg.**

5. Click on **Tool #1 OD ROUGH RIGHT** and make changes in the Toolpath parameters page as shown below:

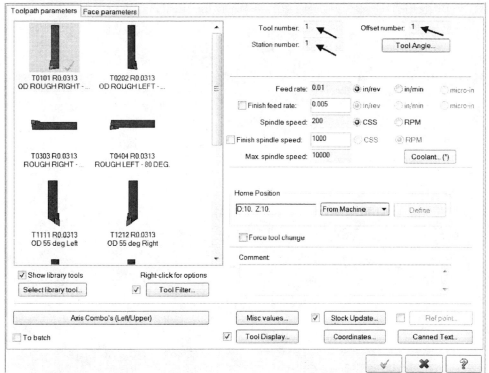

6. Select the **Face parameters** page as shown below:

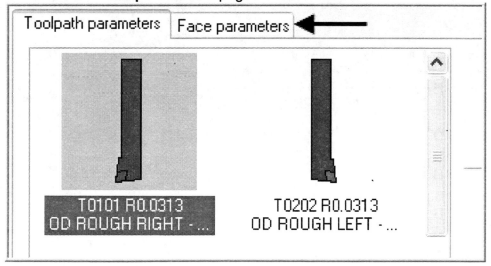

7. Make changes as shown below:

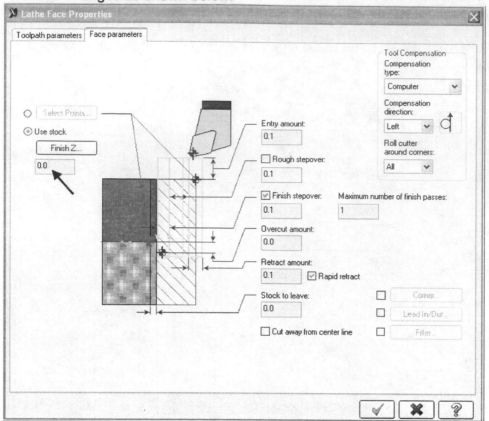

8. Select the OK button [✓] to complete this **Lathe Face** operation.
9. Your screen should look like the image below:

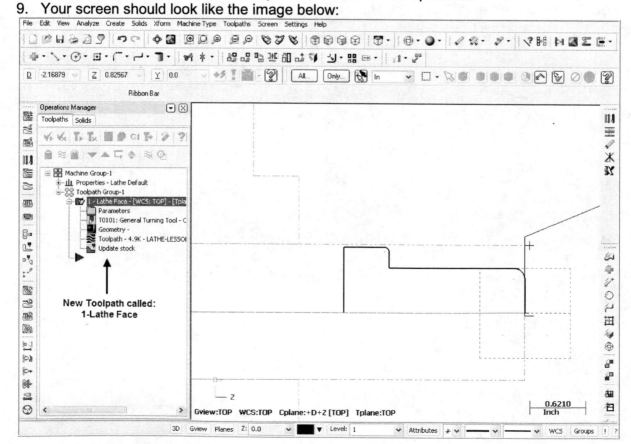

New Toolpath called:
1-Lathe Face

⮷ Note: the new Toolpath called **1-Lathe Face**. This is where all the toolpath information is kept. If changes are required to this toolpath just click on the parameter icon

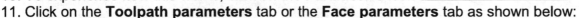 and the Screens from steps 5 and 7 will be available. This is handy in case a mistake was made in setting the toolpath parameters or in case a modification needs to be made.

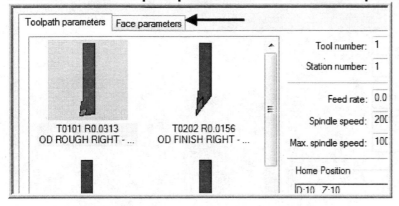

10. To experience how this works, click on the **Parameters** icon
11. Click on the **Toolpath parameters** tab or the **Face parameters** tab as shown below:

⮷ As you can see, all the toolpath settings (parameters) are available in case a change or correction is required.

12. Click on the OK button to return to the main screen.

TASK 8:
ROUGH THE OUTSIDE DIAMETERS
⮷ In this task you will use the same tool as used for the previous facing operation **Tool #1 an OD Rough- Right – 80 deg.**

1. From the menu bar select **Toolpaths>Rough…**

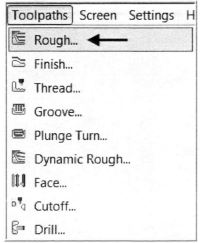

2. In the **Chaining** window Chaining mode is set to **Partial** by default.

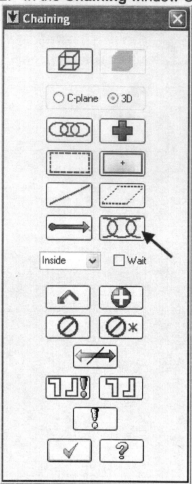

3. Select **Arc 1** as the start of the **Partial chain**.

After you have selected the line **ensure** that the arrow is pointing up as shown below: If it is not select the reverse button in the Chaining dialog box:

4. Then select **Line 2** as the end entity in this chain.

Select the outer boundary or select the retraction point or select done

5. Select the **OK** button ✓ to exit the Chaining dialog window.

6. In the **Toolpath parameters** page select the same tool used to face the part **Tool #1 OD ROUGH RIGHT** and make sure the settings are the same as shown below:

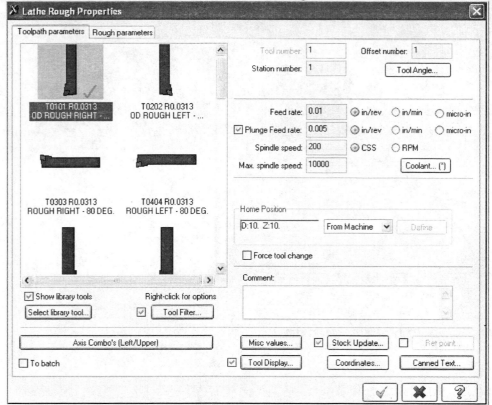

7. Select the **Rough parameters** page and make changes as shown below:

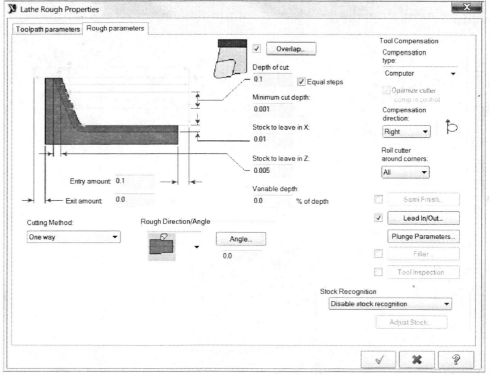

8. Select the **Lead In/Out** button select the **Lead out** page and extend the contour by .2 as shown below:

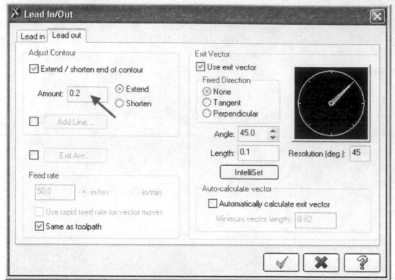

9. Select the **OK** button to exit this function.
10. Select the **OK** button to exit Rough Parameters.

TASK 9:
FINISH THE OUTSIDE DIAMETERS

➲ In this task you will finish the outside diameters in one cut using **Tool #1 an OD Rough-Right – 80 deg.**

1. From the menu bar select **Toolpaths>Finish...**

2. Select **Last** in the Chaining dialog box.

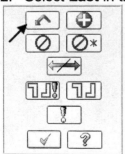

3. Select the **OK** button to complete the selection.

4. Select the same tool used to rough the part; **Tool #1 OD Rough Right** tool from the tool list and make changes as shown below:

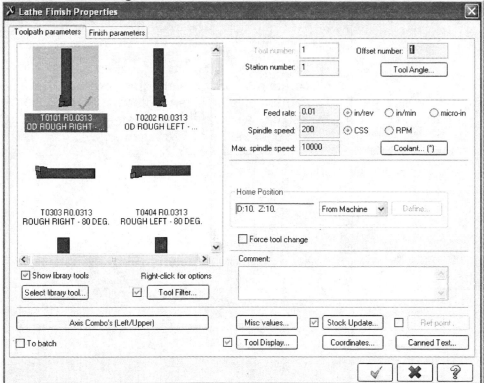

5. Select the **Finish parameters** page and make changes as shown below:

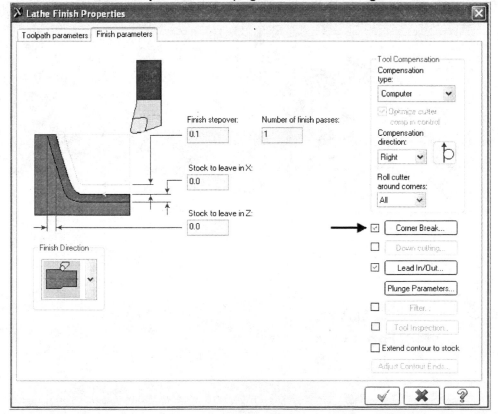

Corner Break: Select the check box to automatically create radii or chamfers on all outer corners of the toolpath. Click the button to edit the corner break settings.

6. Select the **Corner Break** button and make changes as shown below:

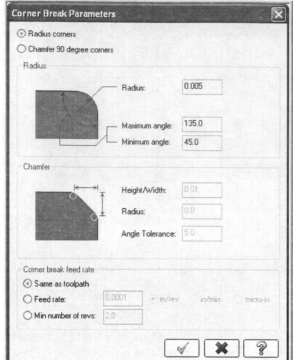

Corner Break
Use this dialog box to automatically create radii or chamfers on all outer corners of lathe finish toolpaths.
You can also set the feed rate when the tool creates the radii or chamfers.

7. Select the OK button to complete this feature.
8. Select the **Lead In/Out** button select the **Lead out** page and extend the contour by .2 as shown below:

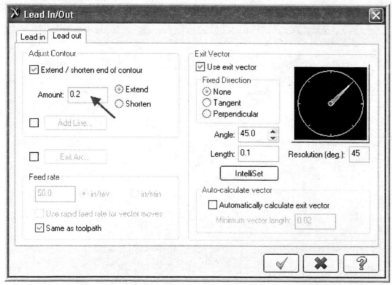

9. Select the **OK** button to exit this function.
10. Select the **OK** button to exit **Finish parameters.**

TASK 10:
CUTOFF THE PART

➲ In this task you will cutoff the part using a .125 wide cutoff tool.

1. From the menu bar select **Toolpaths>Cutoff...**

2. Select the **Alt key** and the **T** key on the keyboard to hide the toolpath lines.

Toolpath Lines visible:	**Press Alt T to hide toolpath Lines:**

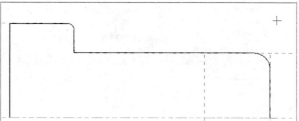

3. Move the cursor over the corner (where **Line 1** and **Line 2** meet) until the visual cue for End point displays and then click on this point as shown below:

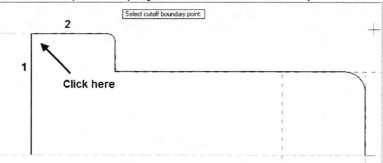

4. Scroll down if required in the tool window and select the **OD Cutoff Right Width .125** tool and make changes as shown below in the **Toolpath parameters** page:

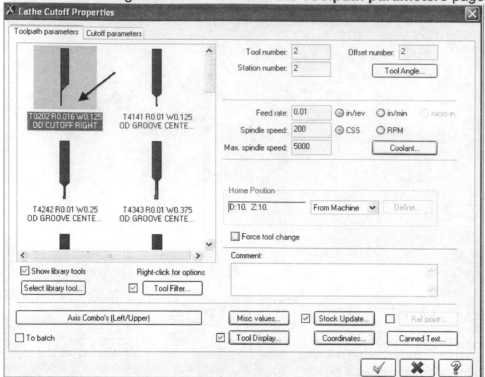

5. Select the **Cutoff parameters** page and make changes as shown below:

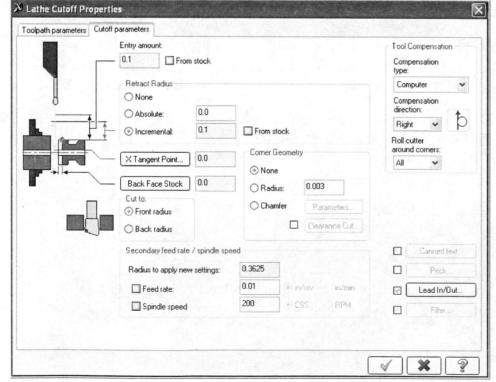

6. Select the **OK** button to exit **Cutoff parameters**.

TASK 11:
BACKPLOT THE TOOLPATH

➲ In this task you will use Mastercam's Backplot function to view the path the tools take to cut this part.

➲ Backplot will enable you to review the cutting motions and identify any problem areas when cutting the part.

➲ When the toolpaths are being Backplotted Mastercam displays tool path information on the right of the screen. Information such as the current tool position in X and Z coordinates.

➲ **For more information on Backplot see the Tips and Techniques section on the multimedia DVD supplied with this text.**

1. To pick all the operations to backplot pick the **Select All** icon 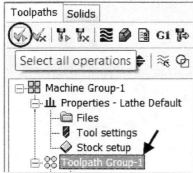 circled below:

➲ Another method to **Select all** the operations is by clicking on the **Toolpath Group-1** in the Toolpaths Manager as shown by the arrow above.

2. The next step is to select the **Backplot selected operations** icon shown below:

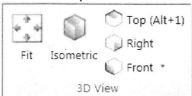

3. **Maximize** the Backplot/Verify window if required.
4. Select the **Home** Tab if required.

5. At the top of the screen select the **Isometric** icon and then select **Fit**.

6. Activate the options shown below in the **Visibility** section of the Home tab.

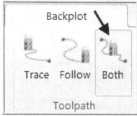

7. Click on the **Backplot** tab at the top left of the screen

8. Activate the **Both** option in the Toolpath section of the Backplot tab.

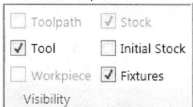

9. In the lower right corner of the screen now set the run **Speed** to slow by moving the slider bar pointer over to the left as shown below.

Speed:

10. Now select the **Play Simulation** button to review the toolpaths.

11. Now hit the **rewind** button on the controls to move back to the **start** position.
12. Select the **Home** Tab and activate the options shown below in the **Visibility** section of the Home tab, activate **Tool** and **Fixtures** only.

13. After reviewing the Backplot of the toolpaths select the **Close** button to exit Backplot.

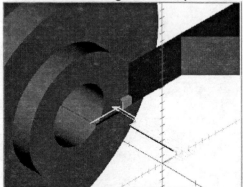

TASK 12:
VERIFY THE TOOLPATH

- ➲ Mastercam's Verify utility allows you to use solid models to simulate the machining of a part. The model created by the verification represents the surface finish, and shows collisions, if any exist.
- ➲ This allows you to identify and correct program errors before they reach the shop floor.
- ➲ Backplot and Verify are very similar. The differences between these two functions are that Backplot offers basic simulation options. Whereas Verify offers material removal, collision checking and precision control.
- ➲ **For more information on Verify see the Tips and Techniques section on the multimedia DVD supplied with this text**

1. In the **Toolpaths Manager** pick all the operations to verify by picking the **Select All** icon

2. Select the **Verify selected operations** icon shown below:

3. **Maximize** the Backplot/Verify window if required.
4. At the top of the screen select the **Isometric** icon and then select **Fit**.

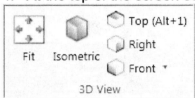

5. Activate the options shown below in the **Visibility** section of the Home tab. **Initial Stock not activated.**

☐ Toolpath	☑ Stock
☑ Tool	☐ Initial Stock
☐ Workpiece	☑ Fixtures
Visibility	

6. Activate the **Color Loop** to change the color of the tools for the verified part.

Color Loop

7. In the lower right corner of the screen now set the run **Speed** to slow by moving the slider bar pointer over to the left as shown below.

Speed:

8. Now select the **Play Simulation** button to review the toolpaths.

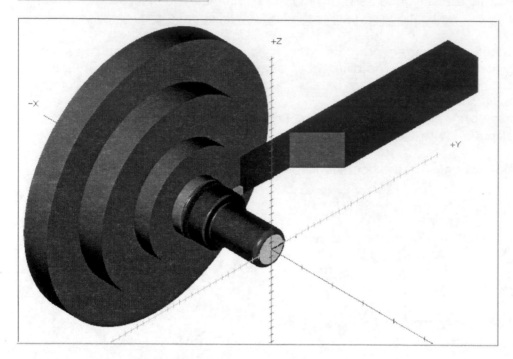

9. Select the **Close** button 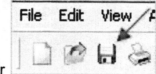 in the top right hand corner to exit Verify.

TASK 13:
SAVE THE UPDATED MASTERCAM FILE

1. Select the **save** icon from the toolbar

TASK 14:
POST AND CREATE THE CNC CODE FILE

1. Ensure all the operations are selected by picking the **Select All** icon  from the Toolpaths manager.

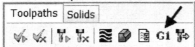

2. Select the **Post selected operations** button from the Toolpaths manager.
➲ **Please Note:** If you cannot see **G1** click on the right pane of the Toolpaths manager window and expand the window to the right.

3. In the Post processing window, make the necessary changes as shown below:

About Post Processing

NC file:
Select this option to save the NC file. The file name and extension are stored in the machine group properties for the selected operation. If you are posting operations from different machine groups or Mastercam files, or batch processing, Mastercam will create several files according to the settings for each machine group.

Edit:
When checked, automatically launches the default text editor with the file displayed so that you can review or modify it.

4. Select the OK button [✓] to continue.

5. Ensure the same name as your Mastercam part file name is displayed in the **NC File name** field as shown below:

File name:	LATHE-LESSON-1.NC
Save as type:	NC Files (*.NC)

6. Select the **Save** button.
7. The CNC code file opens up in the default editor.

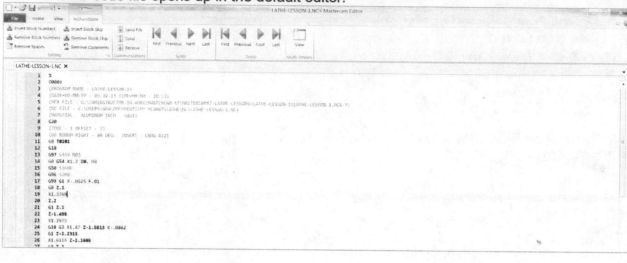

8. Select the [X] in the top right corner to exit the CNC editor.
9. This completes LATHE-LESSON -1.

LATHE-LESSON-1 EXERCISE

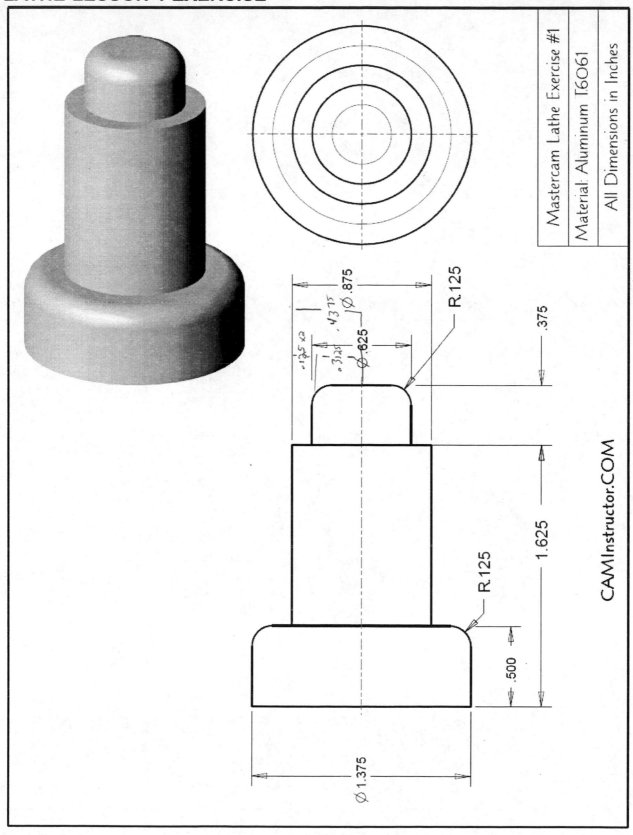

Mastercam Lathe Exercise #1

Material: Aluminum T6061

All Dimensions in Inches

Ø.875

Ø.625

R.125

.375

.125 x2

.3125

.4375

R.125

1.625

.500

Ø 1.375

CAMInstructor.COM

Mastercam. X⁷
TRAINING
GUIDE

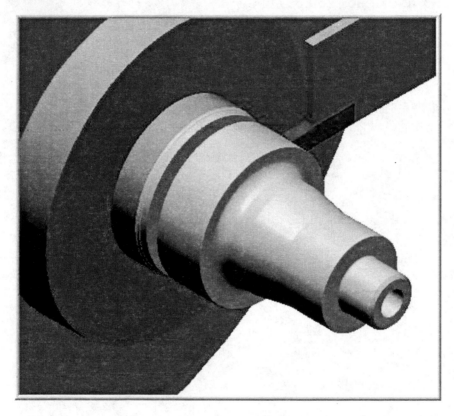

LATHE-LESSON-2
FACE, ROUGH, FINISH, DRILL AND
CUTOFF

camInstructor

Objectives

You will create the geometry for Lathe Lesson 2, and then generate a toolpath to machine the part on a CNC lathe. This lesson covers the following topics:

➲ **Create a 2-dimensional drawing by:**
Creating lines.
Creating fillets.
Creating chamfers.

➲ **Establish Stock and Chuck Setup settings:**
Stock size.
Chuck Configuration.
Material for the part.
Feed calculation.

➲ **Generate a 2-dimensional lathe toolpath consisting of:**
Lathe Face.
Lathe Rough.
Lathe Finish.
Lathe Drill.
Lathe Cutoff.

➲ **Inspect the toolpath using Mastercam's Verify and Backplot by:**
Launching the Verify function to machine the part on the screen.
Using Backplot to identify the accuracy of the toolpaths.
Generating the NC- code.

LATHE - LESSON - 2 DRAWING

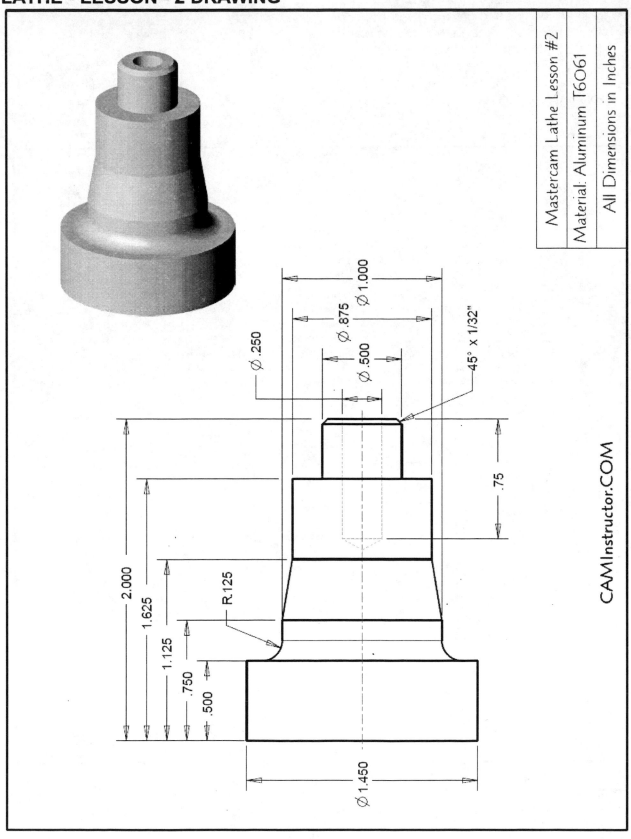

TOOL LIST

Five tools will be used to create this part.
- ⟳ Tool #1 Face and Rough the outside diameters
- ⟳ Tool #2 Finish the outside diameters
- ⟳ Tool #3 Centre drill the hole
- ⟳ Tool #4 Drill the .25 diameter hole
- ⟳ Tool #5 Cutoff the part

```
          Tool List of LATHE-LESSON-2.MCX-5


    Proj./Part No.: 0                    Date       : 06/21/10
    Drawing No.   : 1                    Customer   : -
    Prog. No.     : 1                    Programmer : 1


             Tool type      : T0101: specific tool type - OD ROUGH RIGHT - 80 DEG.
             Manufact.code  :
             Holder/Insert  : DCGNR-164D / CNMG-432
             Setup length   :
             Spindle RPM    :   200     Feedrate UPR :    0.01    Corner radius :   0.0313
             Length offset  :     1     Tool chan. D,Z:  14    ,     8


             Tool type      : T0202: specific tool type - OD FINISH RIGHT - 35 DEG.
             Manufact.code  :
             Holder/Insert  : MVJNR-164D / VNMG-431
             Setup length   :
             Spindle RPM    :   200     Feedrate UPR :    0.01    Corner radius :   0.0156
             Length offset  :     2     Tool chan. D,Z:  14    ,     8


             Tool type      : T0303: specific tool type - CENTER DRILL- .25 DIA.
             Manufact.code  :
             Holder/Insert  :  /
             Setup length   :
             Spindle RPM    :  1000     Feedrate UPR :    0.01    Corner radius :     0
             Length offset  :     3     Tool chan. D,Z:  10    ,    10


             Tool type      : T0404: specific tool type - DRILL .25 DIA.
             Manufact.code  :
             Holder/Insert  :  /
             Setup length   :
             Spindle RPM    :   200     Feedrate UPR :    0.01    Corner radius :     0
             Length offset  :     4     Tool chan. D,Z:  14    ,     8


             Tool type      : T0505: specific tool type - OD CUTOFF RIGHT
             Manufact.code  :
             Holder/Insert  :  /
             Setup length   :
             Spindle RPM    :   200     Feedrate UPR :    0.01    Corner radius :   0.016
             Length offset  :     5     Tool chan. D,Z:  14    ,     8
```

LESSON #2 - THE PROCESS

Geometry Creation

TASK 1:   Setting the Environment
TASK 2:   Setting the Construction Planes
TASK 3:   Create the Geometry
TASK 4:   Create the.125 Fillet radius and 45° x 1/32" –Chamfer
TASK 5:   Save the Drawing

Toolpath Creation

TASK 6:   Define the Stock and Chuck parameters
TASK 7:   Face the Front of the Part
TASK 8:   Rough the Outside Diameters
TASK 9:   Finish the Outside Diameters
TASK 10:   Center Drill the .25" Hole
TASK 11:   Drill the .25" Hole
TASK 12:   Cut off the Part
TASK 13:   Backplot the Toolpath
TASK 14:   Verify the Toolpath
TASK 15:   Save the Updated Mastercam File
TASK 16:   Post and Create the CNC Code File

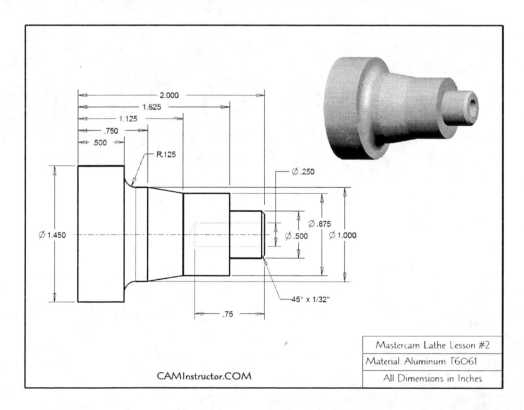

| Mastercam Lathe Lesson #2 |
| Material: Aluminum T6061 |
| All Dimensions in Inches |

CAMInstructor.COM

Geometry Creation

TASK 1:
SETTING THE ENVIRONMENT

Before starting the geometry creation you should set up the grid and toolbars as outlined in the **Setting the Environment** section at the beginning of this text:
1. Set up the Grid. This will help identify the location of the origin.
2. Customize the toolbars to machine a part on the Lathe.
3. Set the machine type to the default Lathe.

TASK 2:
SETTING THE CONSTRUCTION PLANES:

➲ **Set the Construction Plane to Lathe diameter +D +Z (WCS).**
1. Click on **Planes** at the bottom of the screen as shown below:

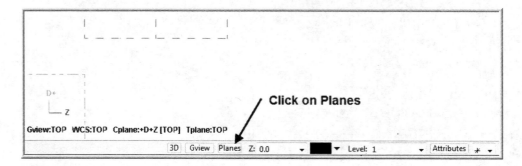

2. Click on **Lathe diameter>+D +Z (WCS)** as shown below:

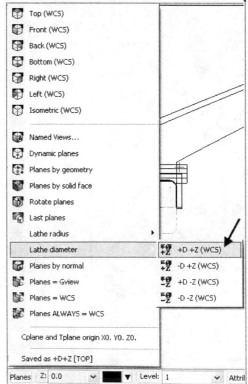

TASK 3:
CREATE THE GEOMETRY – THE LEFT HAND FACE IS AT Z0

➲ This task explains how to create the geometry of this part. In this lathe part you only need to create **half of the geometry**, the geometry above the center line.

➲ Lines 1 through 9 will be created first and then the fillet and chamfer will be created.

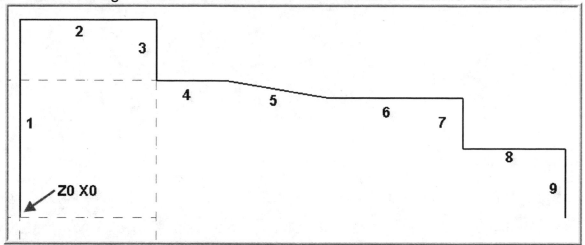

➲ **Create Line #1**

1. Select from the pull down menu **Create>Line>Endpoint...**

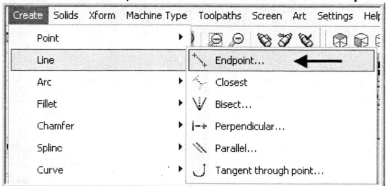

2. The **Line ribbon bar** appears.

3. Move the cursor over the **center of the grid** and as you get close to the origin a visual cue appears. This is the cue that will allow you to snap to the **origin**. With this visual cue highlighted click on the **origin**.

AutoCursor: Visual Cues detects and highlights endpoints and midpoints of curves, lines, arc center points, and point entities. In addition, AutoCursor can snap to angle, nearest, tangent, perpendicular, horizontal, and vertical conditions.

⮑ The following are Mastercam Visual Cues:

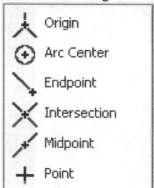
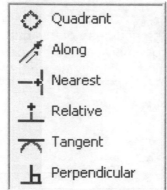

- Origin
- Arc Center
- Endpoint
- Intersection
- Midpoint
- Point
- Quadrant
- Along
- Nearest
- Relative
- Tangent
- Perpendicular

4. You are next prompted to **"Specify the second endpoint"**. On the left hand side of the Line ribbon bar click on the **Multi-Line** button to activate it as shown below by the arrow:

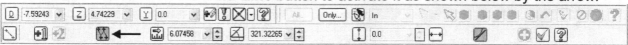

5. Click in the **D** value space (Diameter) (as shown by the arrow below) and enter a value of **1.45**. Hit the Enter key and enter a value of **0 for the Z**, hit the Enter key again and enter a value of **0 for the Y** and hit Enter.

6. A vertical line should be visible as shown below:

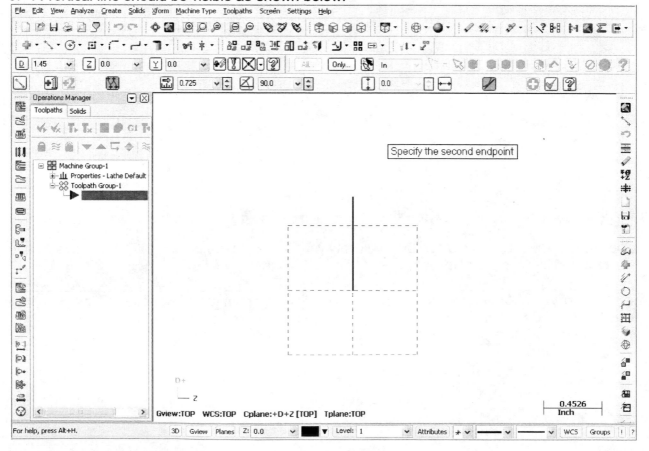

NOTE: If you make a mistake creating lines, click on the **Accept** icon 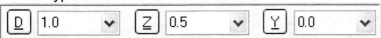 and click on the

Undo icon [↶ ↷]. Then redo the Line.

➲ **Create Line #2**
7. **"Specify the second endpoint"**; Type in **1.45 in D** hit Enter, type in **0.5 in Z** and hit Enter and type in **0.0 in Y** and hit Enter.

➲ **Create Line #3**
8. **"Specify the second endpoint"**; Type in **1.0 in D** hit Enter, type in **0.5 in Z** and hit Enter and type in **0.0 in Y** and hit Enter.

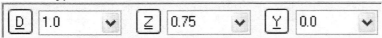

➲ **Create Line #4**
9. **"Specify the second endpoint"**; Type in **1.0 in D** hit Enter, type in **0.75 in Z** and hit Enter and type in **0.0 in Y** and hit Enter.

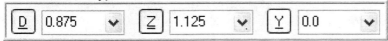

➲ **Create Line #5**
10. **"Specify the second endpoint"**; Type in **0.875 in D** hit Enter, type in **1.125 in Z** and hit Enter and type in **0.0 in Y** and hit Enter.

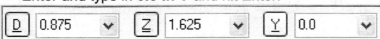

➲ **Create Line #6**
11. **"Specify the second endpoint"**; Type in **0.875 in D** hit Enter, type in **1.625 in Z** and hit Enter and type in **0.0 in Y** and hit Enter.

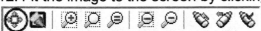

12. Fit the image to the screen by clicking on the Fit to Screen icon as shown below:

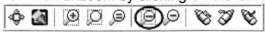

13. Then unzoom by clicking on the **Un-Zoom Previous/ .5** icon as shown below:

➲ **Create Line #7**
14. **"Specify the second endpoint"**; Type in **0.5 in D** hit Enter, type in **1.625 in Z** and hit Enter and type in **0.0 in Y** and hit Enter.

➪ **Create Line #8**

15. **"Specify the second endpoint";** Type in **0.5 in D** hit Enter, type in **2.0 in Z** and hit Enter and type in **0.0 in Y** and hit Enter.

➪ **Create Line #9**

16. **"Specify the second endpoint";** Type in **0.0 in D** hit Enter, type in **2.0 in Z** and hit Enter and type in **0.0 in Y** and hit Enter.

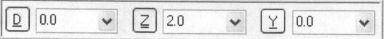

17. Click on the **OK** icon [✓] to complete this feature.

18. Select the **Screen Fit** icon to fit the part to the screen [✦]

19. Your geometry should look like the figure below:

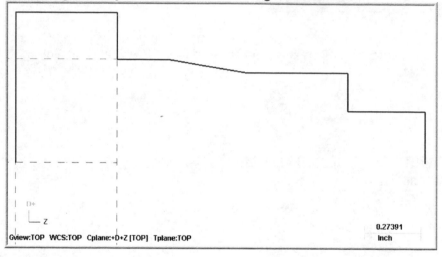

0.27391
Inch
Gview:TOP   WCS:TOP   Cplane:+D+Z [TOP]   Tplane:TOP

TASK 4:
CREATE THE .125 FILLET RADIUS AND 45° X 1/32" –CHAMFER

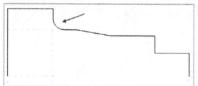

➪ **Create the .125 fillet radius.**

1. Select **Create>Fillet>Entities...**

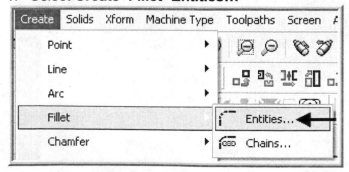

2. The Fillet Entities ribbon bar appears and you are prompted to **"Fillet: Select an entity"**.

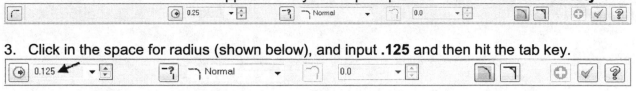

3. Click in the space for radius (shown below), and input **.125** and then hit the tab key.

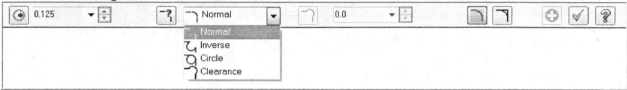

4. You are now transported over to the **Fillet Style field** (shown below). Click on the drop down arrow to review the various fillet radius styles and then ensure **Normal** is selected before moving on.

Normal	
Inverse	
Circle	
Clearance	

Style Field: Sets the fillet style to be created. The following styles are available from the drop down list:

Normal = creates normal fillets on the corners of a contour, resulting in rounded corners.
Inverse = creates inverted arcs on the corners of a contour.
Circle = creates full circles in each of the corners of a contour.
Clearance = creates fillets on inside corners of a contour so that the tool will reach completely into the corner to remove material.

---

5. Ensure the **Trim** option for fillet is activated, the icon is depressed as shown below:

6. Move over to the graphic screen and for the prompt **"Fillet: Select an entity"** click on **Line 1** and then for the prompt **"Fillet: Select another entity"** click on **Line 2** as shown below:

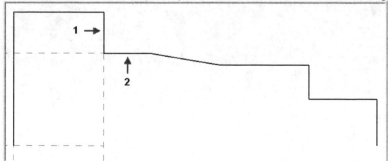

7. Click on the **OK** icon to complete this feature.

8. The completed fillet is shown below:

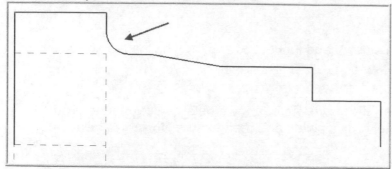

⮥ **Create the 45° x 1/32" (.03125) Chamfer.**

9. Select **Create>Chamfer>Entities...**

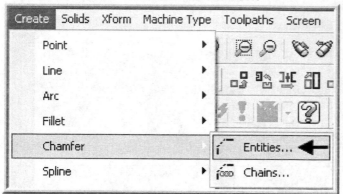

10. The **Chamfer Entities** ribbon bar appears.

11. Click in the space for **distance 1** and input **1/32** and then hit the tab key.

12. This fractional 1/32 will then be converted to a decimal **0.03125** when you hit the tab key.

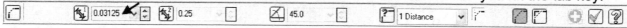

13. You are moved into the **Chamfer Style** options as shown below:

14. Ensure **1 Distance** is selected as shown below:

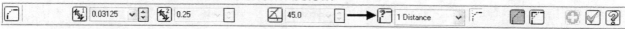

15. Ensure the **Trim** option for Chamfer is activated, the icon is depressed as shown below:

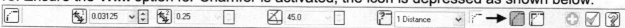

16. Click on **Line 1** and then click on **Line 2** as shown below:

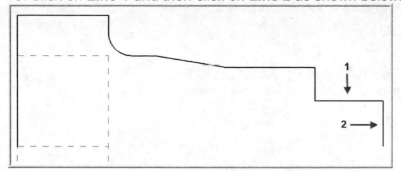

17. Click on the **OK** icon [✓] to complete this feature.
18. The Chamfer should look like the figure below:

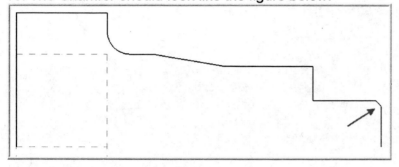

19. This completes the geometry for this part.

TASK 5:
SAVE THE DRAWING

1. Select **File.**
2. Select **Save As...**
3. In the **"File name"** box, type **"Lathe-Lesson-2".**
4. Save to an appropriate location.

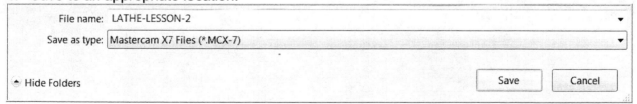

5. Select the Save button to save the file and complete this function.

Toolpath Creation

TASK 6:
DEFINING THE STOCK AND CHUCK PARAMETERS

1. Select the screen fit icon as shown to the right to display the geometry:

2. Ensure your screen looks like the image below:
    a. The Toolpaths Manager is open, if it is not Select Alt and O on your keyboard to open it.
    b. The properties icon displays Lathe Default. If it is not refer to **Setting the Environment** chapter at the beginning of the book.
    c. The Lathe Lesson-2 Geometry is showing.

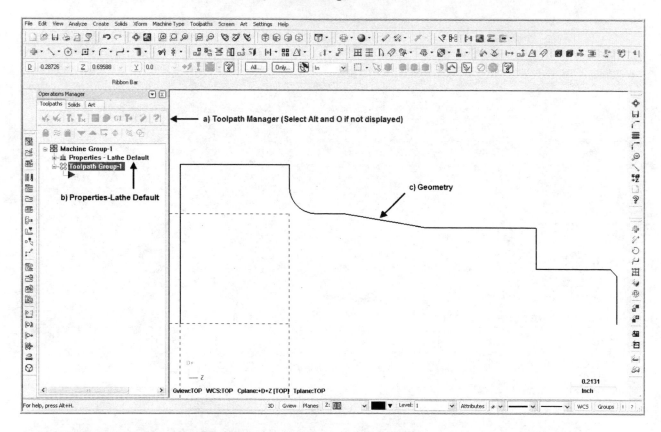

3. Click on the plus in front of **Properties** to expand the Machine Group Properties.

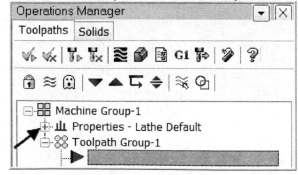

4. **This is Optional -** To expand the toolpaths manager window, click on the outside of the window with the left mouse button (hold the button down) and drag it to the right.

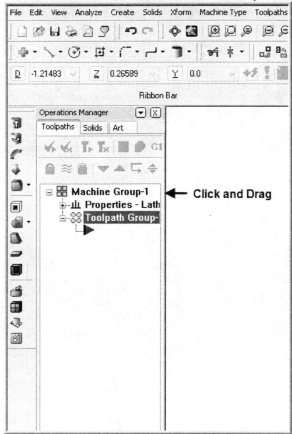

5. Click on **Stock setup** in the Toolpaths Manager window.

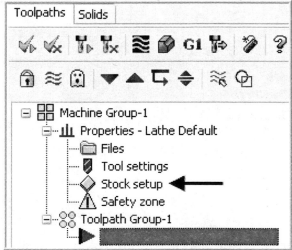

6. Select the **Stock Properties** button in the **Stock Setup** page as shown in the screenshot below:

> ➲ Note: To learn how to complete this section of the **Stock Setup** refer to the **Tips and Techniques** section on the **Mastercam Training Guide – Lathe DVD** that accompanies this book.

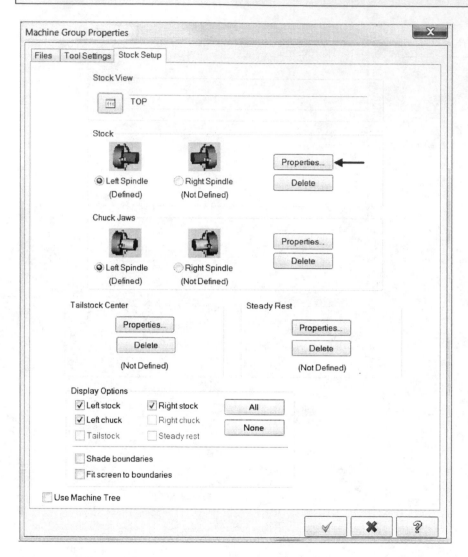

7. In the **Machine Component Manager-Stock** window click on the **Geometry** button and select **Cylinder** as shown below:

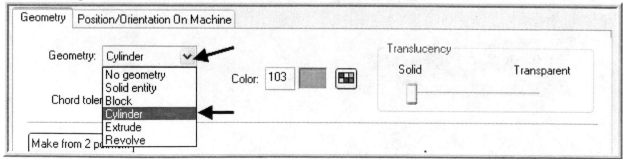

8. In the **Stock setup** set the values as shown below:

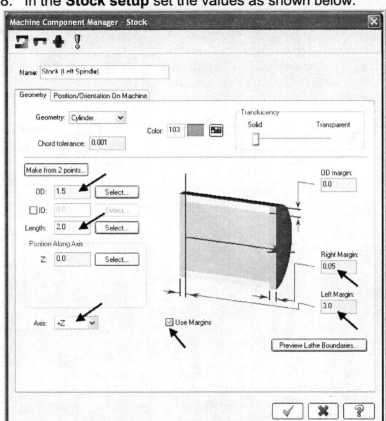

9. Click on the OK icon ✓ to complete this feature.
10. Select the **Chuck Properties** button in the **Stock Setup** page as shown in the screenshot below:

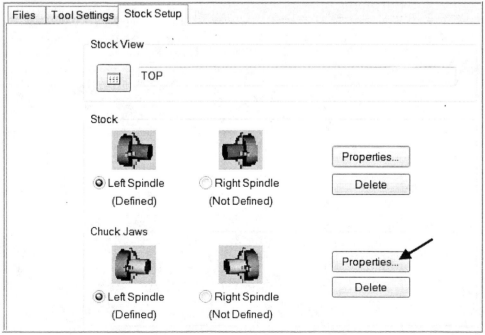

11. In the **Chuck Jaws** setup set the values as shown below:

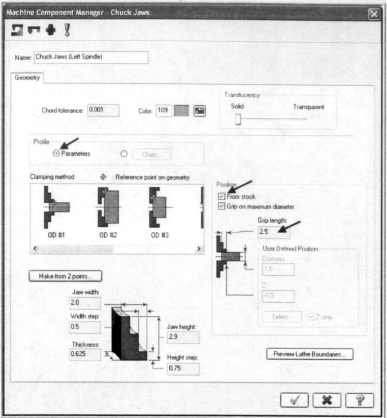

12. Click on the OK icon ✓ to complete this feature.

13. Click on the **Tool Settings** page and make changes as shown below:

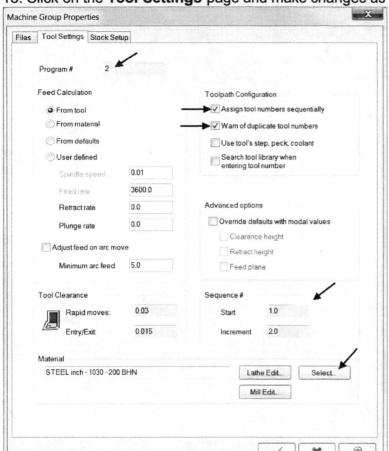

14. To change the **Material** type to Aluminium 6061 pick the **Select** button at the bottom of the Tool Settings page.
15. At the **Material List** dialog box open the Source drop down list and click on **Lathe–library.**

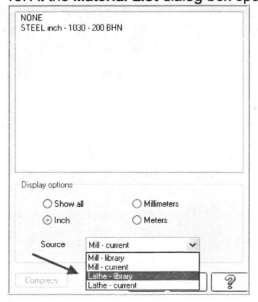

16. From the **Default Materials** list click on **ALUMINIUM inch - 6061** and then click on [✓].

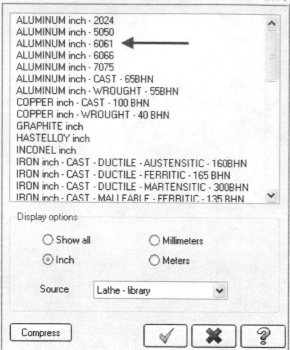

17. Click on the OK button [✓] again to complete this Stock Setup function.

18. Select the **Un Zoom previous / .5** to view the stock setup outline as indicated by broken lines as shown below:

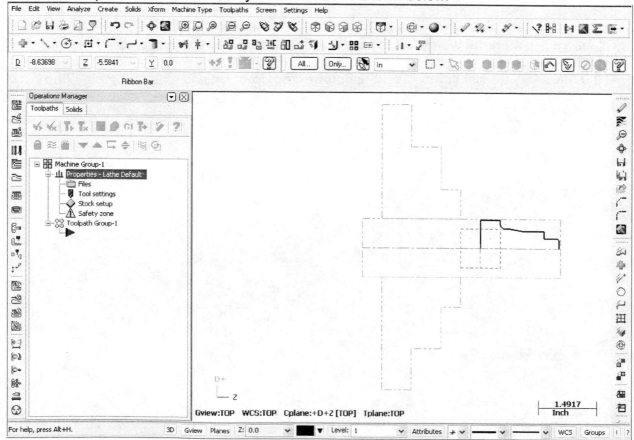

TASK 7:
FACE THE FRONT OF THE PART:

➲ In this task you will use a facing tool to face the front of the part in one cut.

1. Click on the **Screen Fit** icon to fit the part to the screen ⬦.

2. Then click on the **Un-Zoom previous / .5** icon. This function reduces the size of the displayed geometry to 50% of its current size.

3. From the menu bar select **Toolpaths>Face...**

4. When prompted to **"Enter new NC name"** ensure **Lathe-Lesson-2** is entered as shown below and then select the OK button ✓.

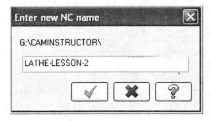

⊃ After selecting the OK button you are confronted with **Toolpath parameters** page. The first task here will be to select **Tool #1 an OD Rough- Right – 80 deg.**

5. Click on **Tool #1** and make changes in the Toolpath parameters page as shown below:

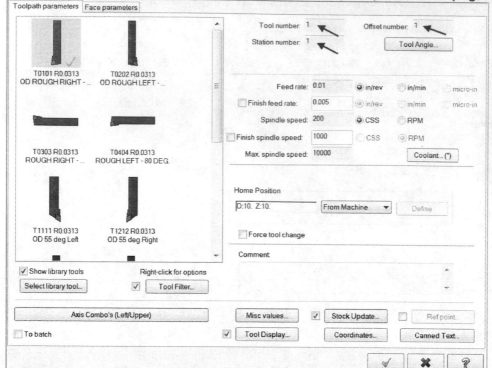

Use the Toolpath parameters tab to: Select a tool, set feeds and speeds, and set other general toolpath parameters.
This tab is very similar for most Lathe toolpaths.

6. Select the **Face parameters** page and make changes as shown below:

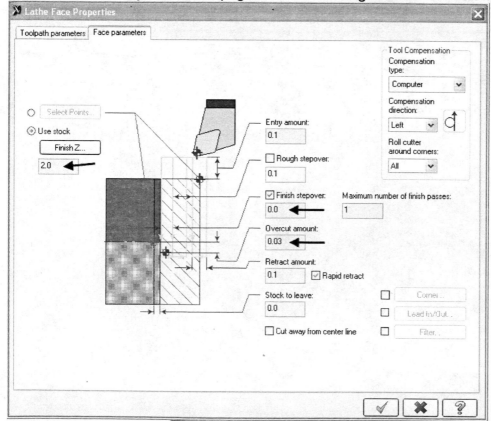

7. Select the OK button 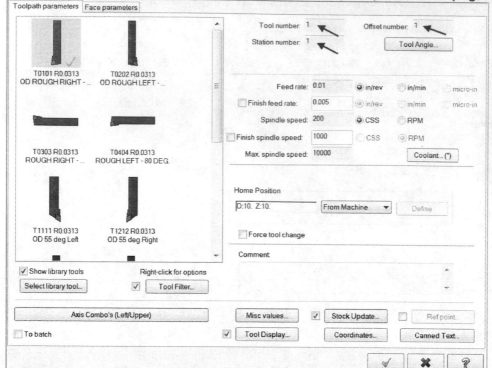 to complete this **Lathe Face** operation.

8. A new Toolpath called **1-Lathe Face** should be displayed as shown below:

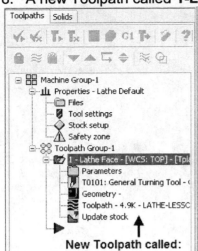

**New Toolpath called:
1-Lathe Face**

➲ Note: the new Toolpath called 1-Lathe Face. This is where all the toolpath information is kept. If changes are required to this toolpath just click on the parameter icon

📁 Parameters   and the Screens from steps 5 and 6 will be available. This is handy in case a mistake was made in setting the toolpath parameters or in case a modification needs to be made.

TASK 8:
ROUGH THE OUTSIDE DIAMETERS

➲ In this task you will use the same tool as used for the previous facing operation **Tool #1 an OD Rough- Right – 80 deg.**

1. From the menu bar select **Toolpaths>Rough…**

2. In the **Chaining** window Chaining mode is set to **Partial** by default.

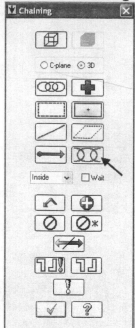

3. Click on chamfer as shown below:

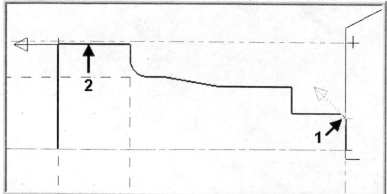

Click on the Chamfer

After you have selected the chamfer **ensure** that the arrow is pointing towards the part as shown below. If it is not select the reverse button in the Chaining dialog box

4. Then select Line 2 as the end entity in this chain.

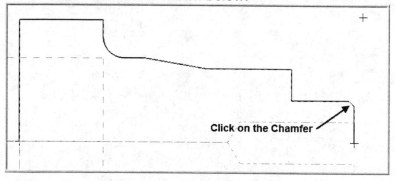

5. Select the OK button to exit the Chaining dialog window.

6. In the **Toolpath parameters** page select the same tool used to face the part **Tool #1 an OD Rough- Right – 80 deg** and make changes as shown below:

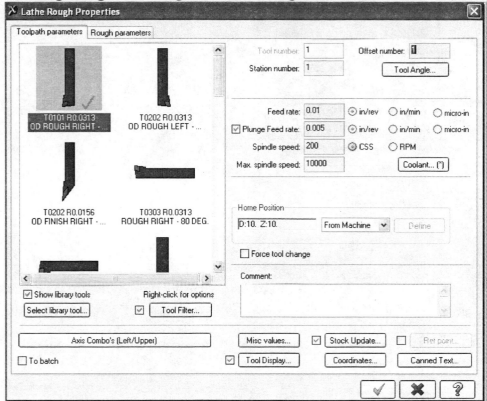

7. Select the **Rough parameters** page and make changes as shown below:

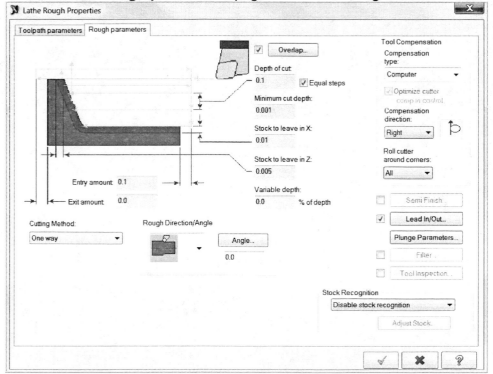

8. Select the **Lead In/Out** button select the **Lead out** page and extend the contour by .2 as shown below:

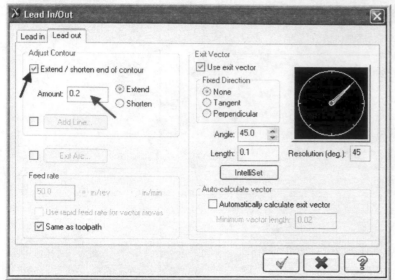

9. Select the OK button 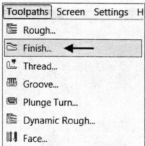 to exit this function.

10. Select the OK button to exit Rough Parameters.

TASK 9:
FINISH THE OUTSIDE DIAMETERS

➲ You will finish the outside diameters in one cut using **Tool #2 OD Finish Right – 35 DEG.**

1. From the menu bar select **Toolpaths>Finish...**

Toolpaths	Screen	Settings	H
📄 Rough...
📂 Finish.. ←
Thread...
Groove...
Plunge Turn...
Dynamic Rough...
Face...

2. Select **Last** in the Chaining dialog box.

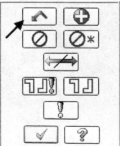

3. Select the OK button to complete the selection.

4. Select **Tool #2 OD Finish Right – 35 DEG** tool from the tool list and make changes as shown below:

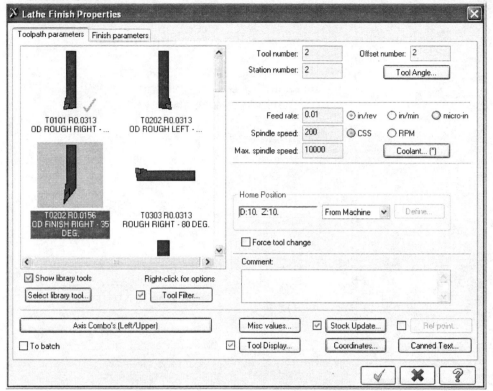

5. Select the **Finish parameters** page and make changes as shown below:

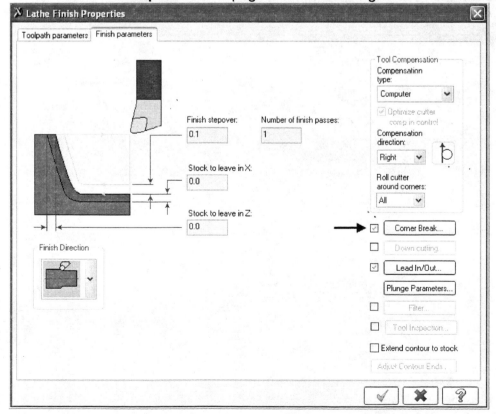

6. Select the Corner Break button and make changes as shown below:

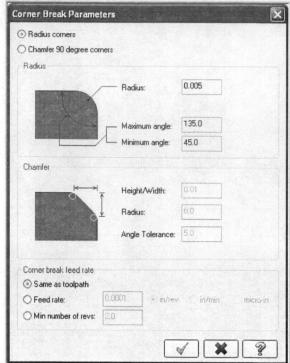

Corner Break
Use this dialog box to automatically create radii or chamfers on all outer corners of lathe finish toolpaths.

You can also set the feed rate when the tool creates the radii or chamfers.

7. Select the OK button [✓] to complete this feature.

8. Select the **Lead In/Out** button select the **Lead in** page and change the Fixed Direction to Tangent as shown below:

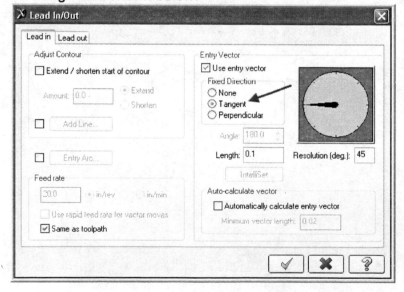

9. Select the **Lead out** page and extend the contour by .2 as shown below:

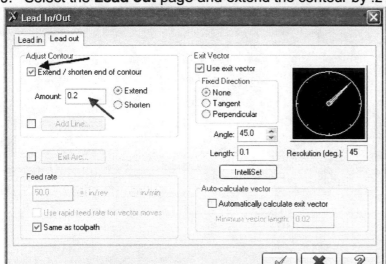

10. Select the OK button [✓] to exit **Lead In/Out.**

11. Select the OK button [✓] to exit **Finish parameters.**

TASK 10:
CENTER DRILL THE .25" HOLE

➲ In this task you will center drill .2" depth using **Tool #3 Centre Drill - .25 diameter.**

1. From the menu bar select **Toolpaths>Drill...**

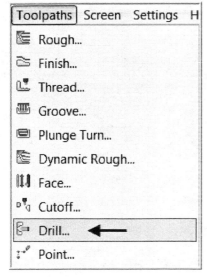

2. Select the **Centre Drill .25 diameter** tool from the tool list and make changes as shown below:

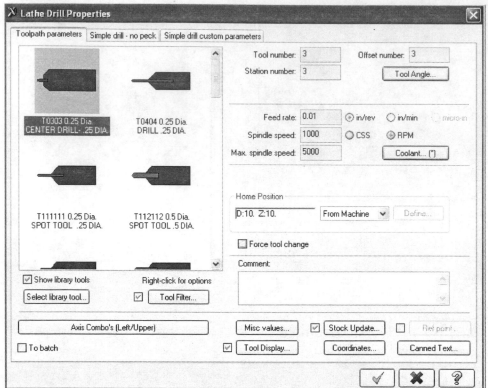

3. Select the **Simple drill – no peck** page and make changes as shown below:

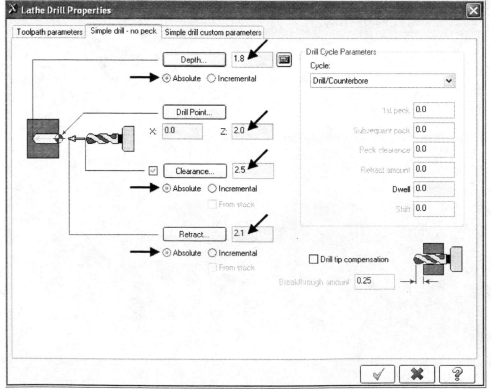

4. Select the OK button [✓] to exit **Simple drill – no peck.**

TASK 11:
DRILL THE .25" HOLE

⊃ In this task you will drill the .25" hole .75" depth using **Tool #4 Drill - .25 diameter.**

1. From the menu bar select **Toolpaths>Drill...**

2. Scroll down and select the **Drill - .25 diameter** tool from the tool list and make changes as shown below:

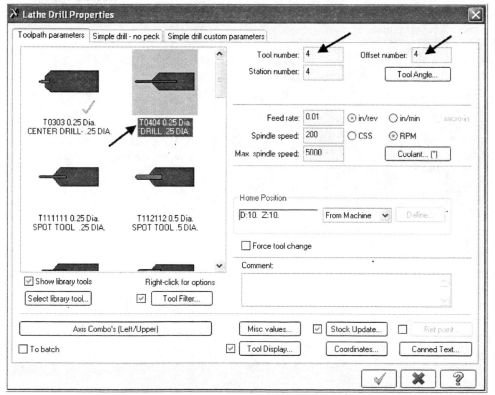

3. Select the **Single drill – no peck** page and make changes as shown below. This hole will be **peck drilled**. The **depth of the hole is .75 from the front face** so click in the space for depth and type in **1.25** and hit the enter key. Make changes as shown below:

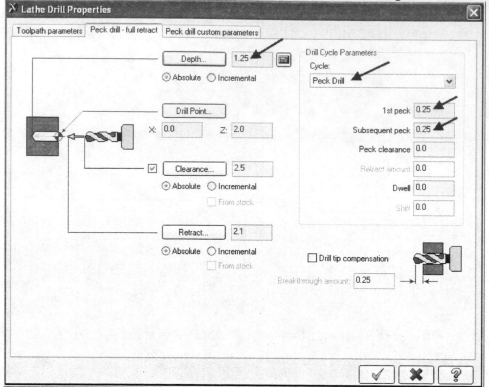

The hole depth on the drawing is dimensioned to .a depth of 0.75" at the full diameter of the hole. So the point of the drill will have to go deeper than 0.75"
You can use the depth calculator button to figure out the correct depth.

4. Select the **Depth Calculator** icon.

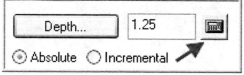

5. Make changes to the **Depth Calculator** as shown below:

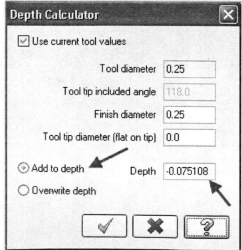

6. Select the **OK** button ☑ to exit **the Depth Calculator.**
7. The depth has now been updated.

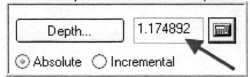

8. Select the **OK** button ☑ to exit **Peck drill – full retract.**

TASK 12:
CUTOFF THE PART

➲ In this task you will cutoff the part using a .125 wide cutoff tool.
1. From the menu bar select **Toolpaths>Cutoff…**

2. Select the Alt key and the T key on the keyboard to hide the toolpath lines.

Toolpath Lines visible: **Press Alt T to hide toolpath Lines:**

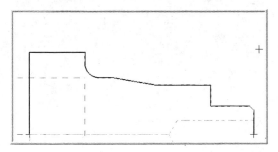

3. Pick where **Line 1 and Line 2** meet as shown below: (Move the cursor over the corner until the visual cue ⬚ for End point displays and then click on this point.)

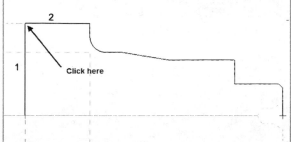

4. Scroll down the tool window and select the **OD Cutoff Right Width .125** tool and make changes as shown below in the **Toolpath parameters** page.

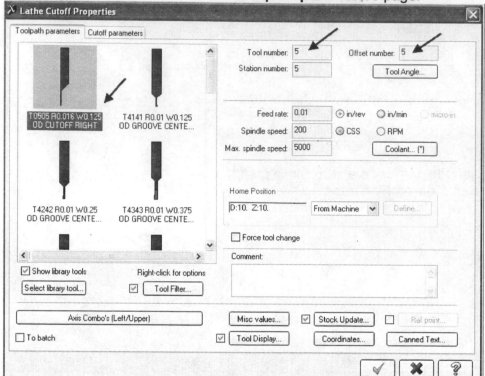

5. Select the **Cutoff parameters** page and make sure the settings are as shown below:

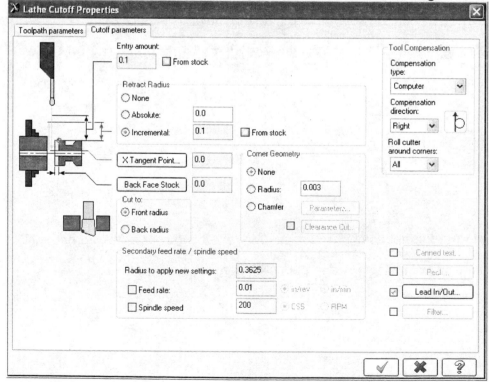

6. Select the OK button [✓] to exit **Cutoff parameters.**

TASK 13:
BACKPLOT THE TOOLPATH

⮞ In this task you will use Mastercam's Backplot function to view the path the tools take to cut this part.

⮞ Backplot will enable us to review the cutting motions and identify any problem areas when cutting the part.

1. Select the **Screen Fit** icon to fit the part to the screen ⬦.

2. Then select the **Un-Zoom previous / .5** icon.  This function reduces the size of the displayed geometry to 50% of its current size.

3. To pick all the operations to backplot pick the **Select All** icon ⬚.

4. The next step is to select the **Backplot selected operations** icon shown below:

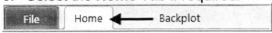

5. **Maximize** the Backplot/Verify window if required.
6. Select the **Home** Tab if required.

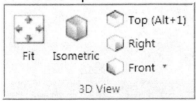

7. At the top of the screen select the **Isometric** icon and then select **Fit**.

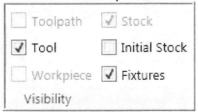

8. Activate the options shown below in the **Visibility** section of the Home tab.

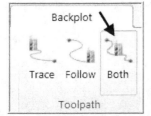

9. Click on the **Backplot** tab at the top left of the screen

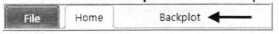

10. Activate the **Both** option in the Toolpath section of the Backplot tab.

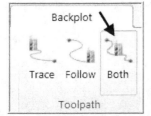

11. In the lower right corner of the screen now set the run **Speed** to slow by moving the slider bar pointer over to the left as shown below.

12. Now select the **Play Simulation** button to review the toolpaths.

13. After reviewing the Backplot of the toolpaths select the Close button [X] to exit Backplot.

TASK 14:
VERIFY THE TOOLPATH

- Mastercam's Verify utility allows you to use solid models to simulate the machining of a part. The model created by the verification represents the surface finish, and shows collisions, if any exist.
- This allows you to identify and correct program errors before they reach the shop floor.
- Backplot and Verify are very similar. The differences between these two functions are that Backplot offers basic simulation options. Whereas Verify offers material removal, collision checking and precision control.
- **For more information on Verify see the Tips and Techniques section on the multimedia DVD supplied with this text**

1. In the Toolpaths Manager pick all the operations to backplot by clicking on the **Select All** icon ⍀ .

2. Select the **Verify selected operations** icon shown below:

3. **Maximize** the Backplot/Verify window if required.
4. At the top of the screen select the Isometric icon and then select Fit.

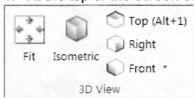

5. Activate the options shown below in the **Visibility** section of the Home tab. **Initial Stock not activated.**

☐ Toolpath	☑ Stock
☑ Tool	☐ Initial Stock
☐ Workpiece	☑ Fixtures
Visibility	

6. Activate the **Color Loop** to change the color of the tools for the verified part.

7. In the lower right corner of the screen now set the run **Speed** to slow by moving the slider bar pointer over to the left as shown below.

Speed: ⎡◯————————⎤

8. Now select the **Play Simulation** button to review the toolpaths.

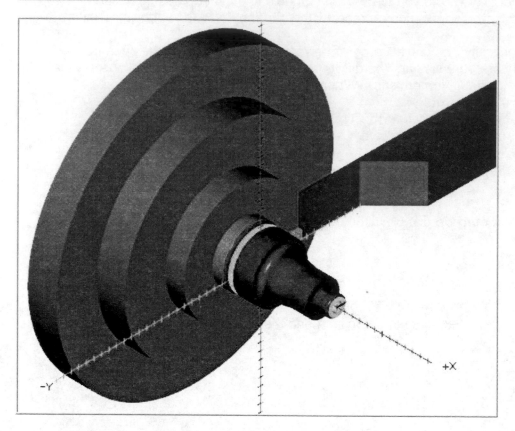

9. Select the **Close** button 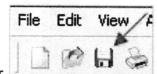 in the top right hand corner to exit Verify.

TASK 15:
SAVE THE UPDATED MASTERCAM FILE

1. Select the save icon from the toolbar

TASK 16:
POST AND CREATE THE CNC CODE FILE

1. Ensure all the operations are selected by picking the **Select All** icon  from the Toolpaths manager.

2. Select the **Post selected operations** button from the Toolpaths manager.
➲ **Please Note:** If you cannot see **G1** click on the right pane of the Toolpaths manager window and expand the window to the right.

3. In the Post processing window, make the necessary changes as shown below:

About Post Processing

NC file:
Select this option to save the NC file. The file name and extension are stored in the machine group properties for the selected operation. If you are posting operations from different machine groups or Mastercam files, or batch processing, Mastercam will create several files according to the settings for each machine group.

Edit:
When checked, automatically launches the default text editor with the file displayed so that you can review or modify it.

4. Select the OK button to continue.

5. Ensure the same name as your Mastercam part file name is displayed in the **NC File name** field as shown below:

6. Select the **Save** button.
7. The CNC code file opens up in the default editor.

8. Select the ⊠ in the top right corner to exit the CNC editor.

9. This completes LATHE-LESSON-2.

LATHE-LESSON-2 EXERCISE

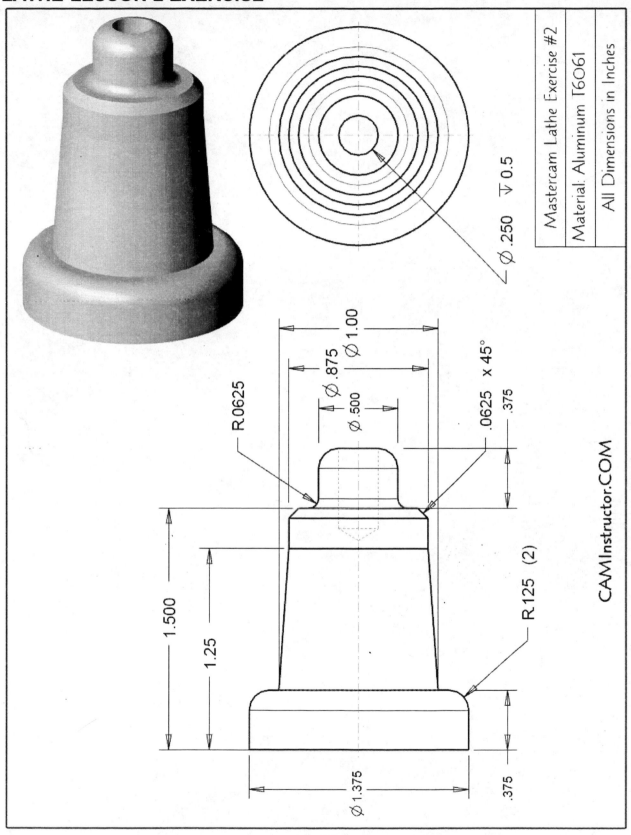

Mastercam Lathe Exercise #2

Material: Aluminum T6061

All Dimensions in Inches

CAMInstructor.COM

∅ .250 ⊽ 0.5

R .0625

∅ 1.00

∅ .875

∅ .500

.0625 x 45°

.375

R 125 (2)

1.500

1.25

∅ 1.375

.375

Mastercam X⁷
TRAINING
GUIDE

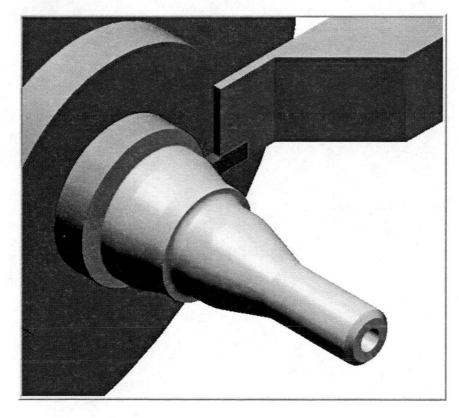

LATHE-LESSON-3
FACE, ROUGH, FINISH, DRILL,
INTERNAL THREAD AND CUTOFF

camInstructor

Objectives

You will create the geometry for Lathe Lesson 3, and then generate a toolpath to machine the part on a CNC lathe. This lesson covers the following topics:

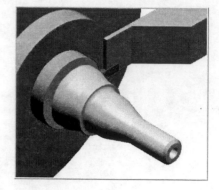

➲ **Create a 2-dimensional drawing by:**
Creating lines.
Creating fillets.
Creating chamfers.

➲ **Establish Stock and Chuck Setup settings:**
Stock size.
Chuck Configuration.
Material for the part.
Feed calculation.

➲ **Generate a 2-dimensional lathe toolpath consisting of:**
Lathe Face.
Lathe Rough.
Lathe Finish.
Lathe Drill and Thread.
Lathe Cutoff.

➲ **Inspect the toolpath using Mastercam's Verify and Backplot by:**
Launching the Verify function to machine the part on the screen.
Generating the NC- code.

LATHE - LESSON - 3 DRAWING

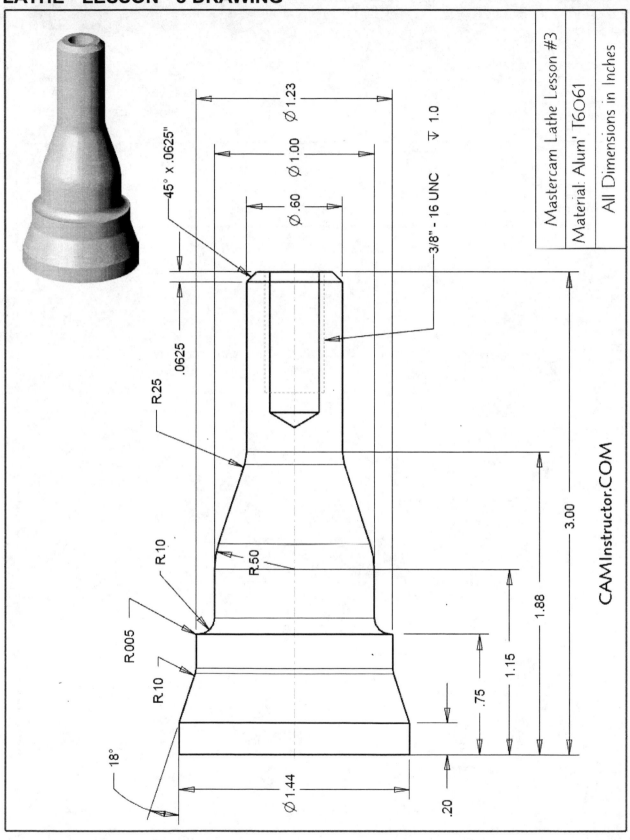

45° x .0625"

Ø 1.23

Ø 1.00

Ø .60

3/8" - 16 UNC   ⌵ 1.0

Mastercam Lathe Lesson #3

Material: Alum' T6061

All Dimensions in Inches

.0625

R.25

R.10

R.50

R.005

R.10

3.00

1.88

1.15

.75

18°

Ø 1.44

.20

CAMInstructor.COM

TOOL LIST

Six tools will be used to create this part.
- ➲ Tool #1 Face and Rough the outside diameters
- ➲ Tool #2 Finish the outside diameters
- ➲ Tool #3 Centre drill the hole
- ➲ Tool #4 Tap Drill the .3125 diameter hole
- ➲ Tool #5 Tap the .375-16 hole
- ➲ Tool #6 Cutoff the part

```
              Tool List of LATHE-LESSON-3.MCX-5

Proj./Part No.: 0                    Date      : 06/24/10
Drawing No.   : 1                    Customer  : -
Prog. No.     : 3                    Programmer : 1
```

Tool type	: T0101: specific tool type - OD ROUGH RIGHT - 80 DEG.
Manufact.code	:
Holder/Insert	: DCGNR-164D / CNMG-432
Setup length	:
Spindle RPM : 200	Feedrate UPR : 0.01 Corner radius : 0.0313
Length offset : 1	Tool chan. D,Z: 14 , 8

Tool type	: T0202: specific tool type - OD FINISH RIGHT - 35 DEG.
Manufact.code	:
Holder/Insert	: MVJNR-164D / VNMG-431
Setup length	:
Spindle RPM : 200	Feedrate UPR : 0.01 Corner radius : 0.0156
Length offset : 2	Tool chan. D,Z: 14 , 8

Tool type	: T0303: specific tool type - CENTER DRILL- .25 DIA.
Manufact.code	:
Holder/Insert	: /
Setup length	:
Spindle RPM : 1000	Feedrate UPR : 0.01 Corner radius : 0
Length offset : 3	Tool chan. D,Z: 10 , 10

Tool type	: T0404: specific tool type - 5/16 DRILL
Manufact.code	:
Holder/Insert	: 5/16 DRILL / 5/16 DRILL
Setup length	:
Spindle RPM : 855	Feedrate UPM : 4.2442 Corner radius : 0
Length offset : 4	Tool chan. D,Z: 10 , 10

Tool type	: T0505: specific tool type - 3/8-16 RH TAP
Manufact.code	:
Holder/Insert	: 3/8-16 RH TAP / 3/8-16 RH TAP
Setup length	:
Spindle RPM : 713	Feedrate UPM : 44.5667 Corner radius : 0
Length offset : 5	Tool chan. D,Z: 10 , 10

Tool type	: T0606: specific tool type - OD CUTOFF RIGHT
Manufact.code	:
Holder/Insert	: /
Setup length	:
Spindle RPM : 200	Feedrate UPR : 0.0025 Corner radius : 0.016
Length offset : 6	Tool chan. D,Z: 14 , 8

LESSON - 3 - THE PROCESS

Geometry Creation

TASK 1:	Setting the Environment
TASK 2:	Setting the Construction Planes
TASK 3:	Create the Geometry
TASK 4:	Create the18 Degree Angle
TASK 5:	Create the Fillets (Radius)
TASK 6:	Create the Chamfer
TASK 7:	Save the Drawing

Toolpath Creation

TASK 8:	Define the Stock and Chuck Parameters
TASK 9:	Face the Front of the Part
TASK 10:	Rough the Outside Diameters
TASK 11:	Finish the Outside Diameters
TASK 12:	Center Drill the 5/16" Hole
TASK 13:	Drill the 5/16" Hole
TASK 14:	Tap the 3/8"-16 Hole
TASK 15:	Cut off the Part
TASK 16:	Verify the Toolpath
TASK 17:	Save the Updated Mastercam File
TASK 18:	Post and Create the CNC Code File

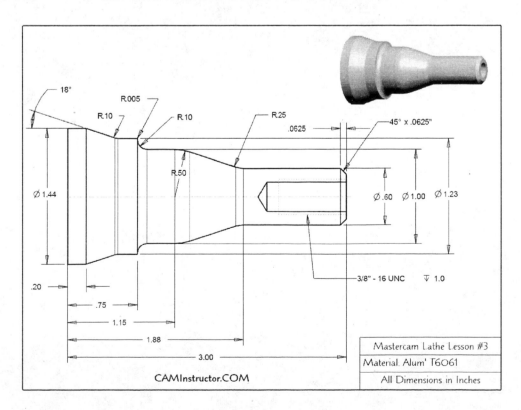

Mastercam Lathe Lesson #3
Material. Alum' T6061
All Dimensions in Inches

CAMInstructor.COM

Geometry Creation

TASK 1:
SETTING THE ENVIRONMENT

Before starting the geometry creation you should set up the grid and toolbars as outlined in the **Setting the Environment** section at the beginning of this text:
1. Set up the Grid. This will help identify the location of the origin.
2. Customize the toolbars to machine a part on the Lathe.
3. Set the machine type to the default Lathe.

TASK 2:
SETTING THE CONSTRUCTION PLANES:

➲ **Set the Construction Plane to Lathe diameter +D +Z (WCS)**
1. Click on Planes at the bottom of the screen as shown below:

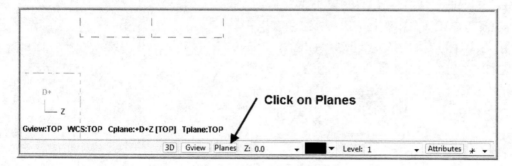

2. Click on Lathe diameter>+D +Z (WCS) as shown below:

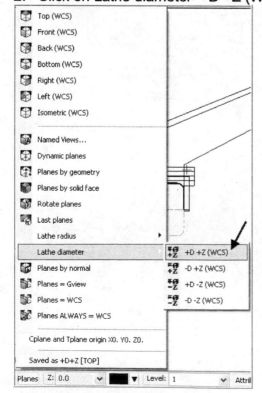

TASK 3:
CREATE THE GEOMETRY

➲ This task explains how to create the geometry of this part. In this lathe part you only need to create **half of the geometry**, the geometry above the center line.

➲ Lines 1 through 9 will be created first and then the fillet and chamfer will be created.

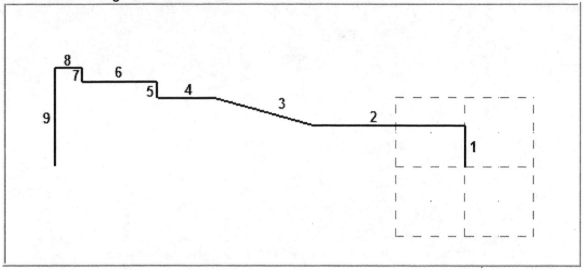

➲ **Create Line #1**

1. Select from the pull down menu **Create>Line>Endpoint…**

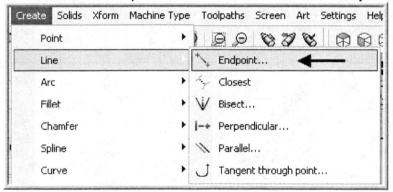

2. The Line ribbon bar appears

3. Move the cursor over the **center of the grid** and as you get close to the origin a visual cue appears. This is the cue that will allow you to snap to the **origin**. With this visual cue highlighted pick the **origin.**

AutoCursor: Visual Cues detects and highlights endpoints and midpoints of curves, lines, arc center points, and point entities. In addition, AutoCursor can snap to angle, nearest, tangent, perpendicular, horizontal, and vertical conditions.

⊃ The following are Mastercam Visual Cues:

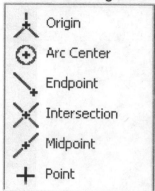

- Origin
- Arc Center
- Endpoint
- Intersection
- Midpoint
- Point

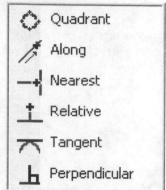

- Quadrant
- Along
- Nearest
- Relative
- Tangent
- Perpendicular

4. You are next prompted to **"Specify the second endpoint"**. On the left hand side of the Line ribbon bar click on the **Multi-Line** button to activate it as shown below by the arrow:

5. Click in the **D** value space (Diameter) (as shown by the arrow below) and enter a value of **0.6**. Hit the Enter key and enter a value of **0 for the Z**, hit the enter key again and enter a value of **0 for the Y** and hit Enter.

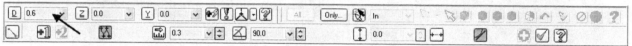

6. A vertical line should be visible as shown below:

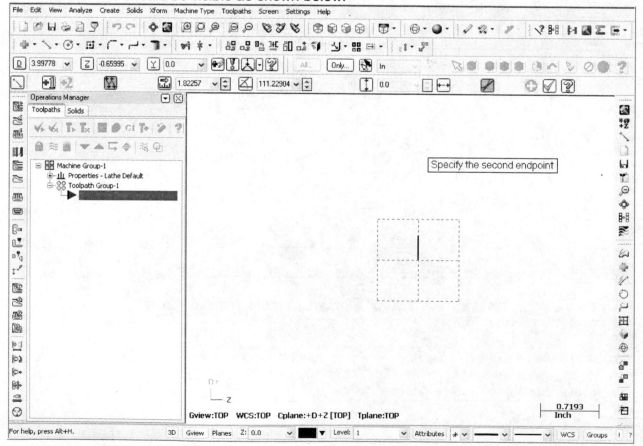

⮑ **Create Line #2**

7. **"Specify the second endpoint"**; Type in **0.6 in D** hit Enter, type in **-1.12 in Z** and hit Enter and type in **0.0 in Y** and hit Enter.

⮑ **Create Line #3**

8. **"Specify the second endpoint"**; Type in **1.0 in D** hit Enter, type in **-1.85 in Z** and hit Enter and type in **0.0 in Y** and hit Enter.

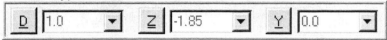

⮑ **Create Line #4**

9. **"Specify the second endpoint"**; Type in **1.0 in D** hit Enter, type in **-2.25 in Z** and hit Enter and type in **0.0 in Y** and hit Enter.

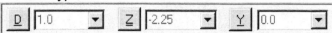

⮑ **Create Line #5**

10. **"Specify the second endpoint"**; Type in **1.23 in D** hit Enter, type in **-2.25 in Z** and hit Enter and type in **0.0 in Y** and hit Enter.

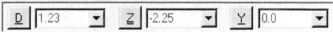

⮑ **Create Line #6**

11. **"Specify the second endpoint"**; Type in **1.23 in D** hit Enter, type in **-2.8 in Z** and hit Enter and type in **0.0 in Y** and hit Enter.

12. Fit the image to the screen by clicking on the **Fit** icon as shown below:

13. Then unzoom by clicking on the **Un-Zoom Previous / .5** icon as shown below:

⮑ **Create Line #7**

14. **"Specify the second endpoint"**; Type in **1.44 in D** hit Enter, type in **-2.8 in Z** and hit Enter and type in **0.0 in Y** and hit Enter.

⮑ **Create Line #8**

15. **"Specify the second endpoint"**; Type in **1.44 in D** hit Enter, type in **-3.00 in Z** and hit Enter and type in **0.0 in Y** and hit Enter.

⇨ **Create Line #9**

16. **"Specify the second endpoint";** Type in **0.0 in D** hit Enter, type in **-3.0 in Z** and hit Enter and type in **0.0 in Y** and hit Enter.

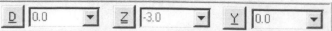

17. Click on the **OK** icon [✓] to complete this feature.

18. Select the **Screen Fit** icon to fit the part to the screen [✦].

19. Your geometry should look like the figure below.

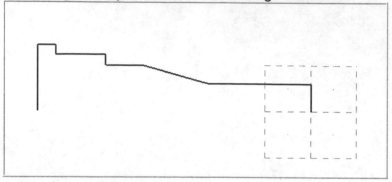

TASK 4:
CREATE THE 18 DEGREE ANGLE

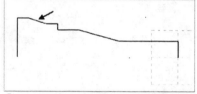

Create the 18 Degree Angle.

1. Select **Create>Line>Endpoint...**

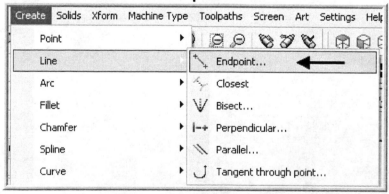

2. The Create Line ribbon bar appears and you are prompted to **"Specify the first endpoint".**

3. Click on the end of line 8 as shown below:

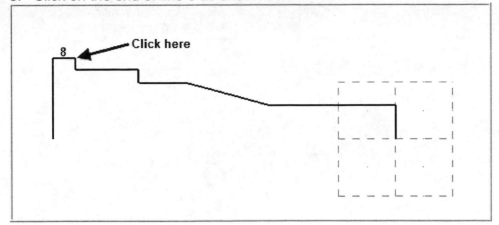

4. Click in the space for Length (#1 below) and input **-1.0** and then hit the tab key. Enter **180-18** (#2 below) and hit Enter.

5. A new line is drawn as shown below:

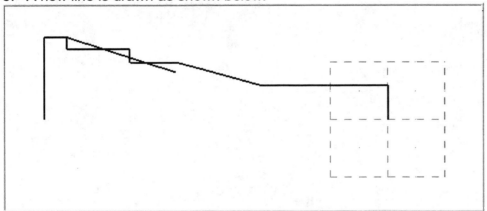

6. Click on the OK icon ✓ to complete this feature.
7. Select **Edit>Trim/Break>Trim/Break/Extend**.

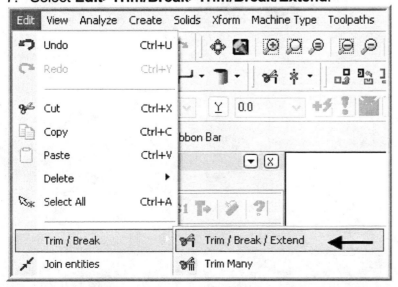

8. Click on the Trim 2 Entity Icon as shown below:

9. Click on line 1 and then line 2 as shown below:

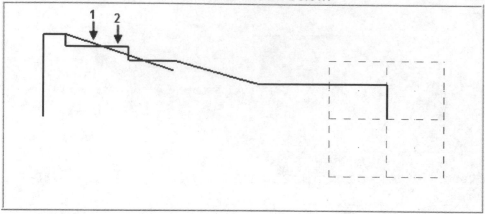

10. The line is trimmed as shown below:

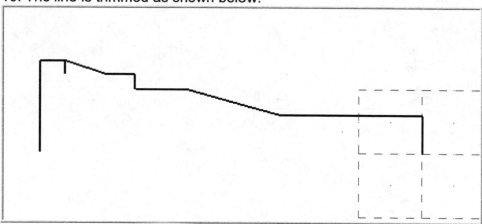

11. Click on the **OK** icon ☑ to complete this feature.

12. Click on the line as shown below and hit the **Delete** key on your computer keyboard.

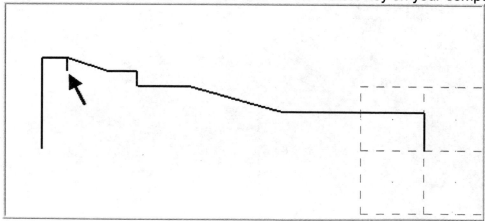

TASK 5:
CREATE THE FILLETS (RADIUS)

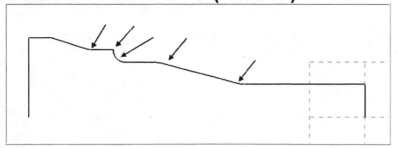

1. Select **Create>Fillet>Entities...**

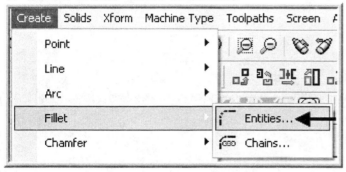

2. Click in the space for radius (shown below), and input **.10** and then hit the tab key.

3. You are now transported over to the **Fillet Style field** (shown below). Click on the drop down arrow to review the various fillet radius styles and then ensure **Normal** is selected before moving on.

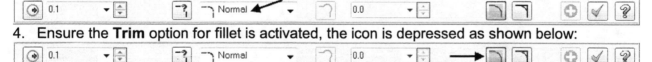

4. Ensure the **Trim** option for fillet is activated, the icon is depressed as shown below:

5. Move over to the graphic screen and for the prompt **"Fillet: Select an entity"** click on **Line 1** and then for the prompt **"Fillet: Select another entity"** click on **Line 2** as shown below:

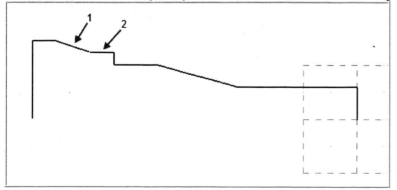

6. Click on the **Apply** icon to complete this feature.

7. Click in the space for radius (shown below), and input **0.005** and then hit the tab key.

8. For the prompt **"Fillet: Select an entity"** click on **Line 1** and then for the prompt **"Fillet: Select another entity"** click on **Line 2** as shown below:

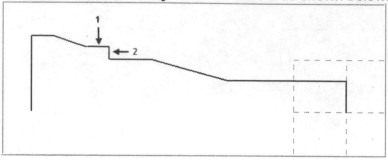

9. Click on the **Apply** 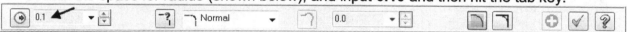 icon to complete this feature.

10. Click in the space for radius (shown below), and input **0.10** and then hit the tab key.

11. For the prompt **"Fillet: Select an entity"** click on **Line 1** and then for the prompt **"Fillet: Select another entity"** click on **Line 2** as shown below:

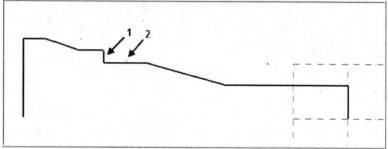

12. Click on the **Apply** icon to complete this feature.

13. Click in the space for radius (shown below), and input **0.50** and then hit the tab key.

14. For the prompt **"Fillet: Select an entity"** click on **Line 1** and then for the prompt **"Fillet: Select another entity"** click on **Line 2** as shown below:

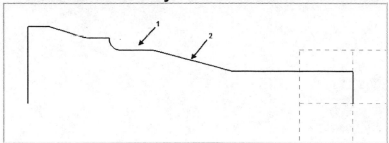

15. Click on the **Apply** ⊕ icon to complete this feature.
16. Click in the space for radius (shown below), and input **0.25** and then hit the tab key.

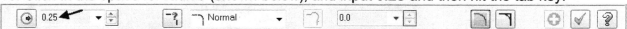

17. For the prompt **"Fillet: Select an entity"** click on **Line 1** and then for the prompt **"Fillet: Select another entity"** click on **Line 2** as shown below:

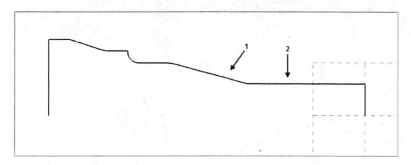

18. Click on the **OK** icon ✓ to complete this feature.

19. The completed fillet is shown below:

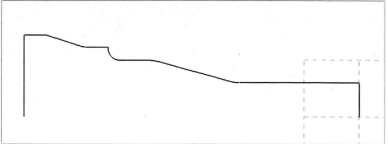

TASK 6:
CREATE THE CHAMFER

1. Select **Create>Chamfer>Entities...**

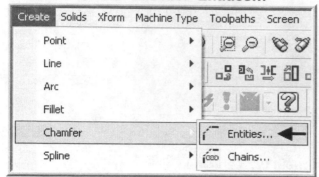

2. The **Chamfer Entities** ribbon bar appears.

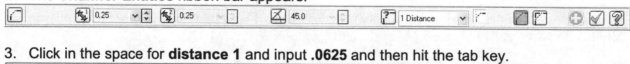

3. Click in the space for **distance 1** and input **.0625** and then hit the tab key.

4. Ensure the 1 Distance option for **Chamfer Style** is selected as shown below:

5. Ensure the **Trim** option for Chamfer is activated, the icon is depressed as shown below:

6. Move over to the graphic screen and for the prompt **"Select Line or arc"** click on **Line 1** and then for the prompt **"Select Line or arc"** click on **Line 2** as shown below:

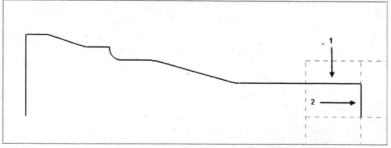

7. Click on the **OK** icon [✓] to complete this feature.
8. The Chamfer should look like the figure below:

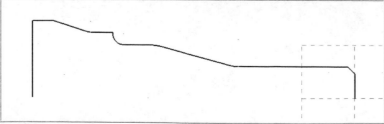

9. This completes the geometry for this part.

TASK 7:
SAVE THE DRAWING

1. Select **File**.
2. Select **Save as**.
3. In the "File name" box, type "Lathe-Lesson-3".
4. Save to an appropriate location.
5. Select the Save button to save the file and complete this function.

Toolpath Creation

TASK 8:
DEFINE THE STOCK AND CHUCK PARAMETERS

1. Ensure your screen looks like the image below:
   a. The Toolpath Manager is open, if it is not Select Alt and O on your keyboard to open it.
   b. The properties icon displays Lathe Default. If it is not refer to **Setting the Environment** chapter at the beginning of the book.
   c. The Lathe Lesson-3 Geometry is showing.
2. Select the screen fit icon as shown below to display the geometry:

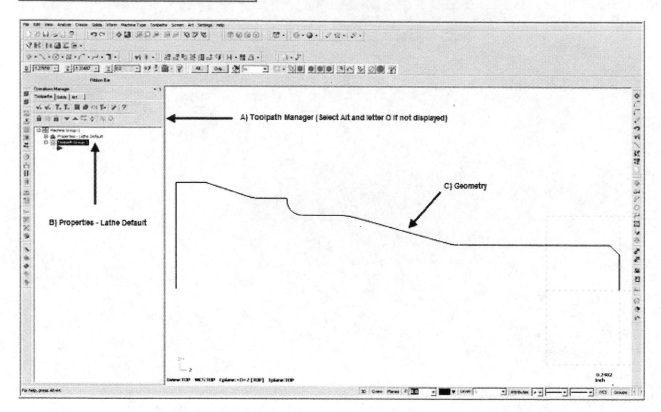

3. Select the plus in front of **Properties** to expand the Machine Group Properties.

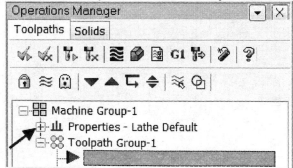

4. Select **Stock setup** in the toolpath manager window.

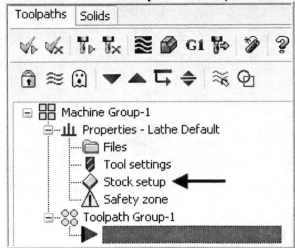

5. Select the **Stock Properties** button in the **Stock Setup** page as shown in the screenshot below:

➲ Note: To learn how to complete this section of the **Stock Setup** refer to the **Tips and Techniques** section on the **Mastercam Training Guide – Lathe CD** that accompanies this book.

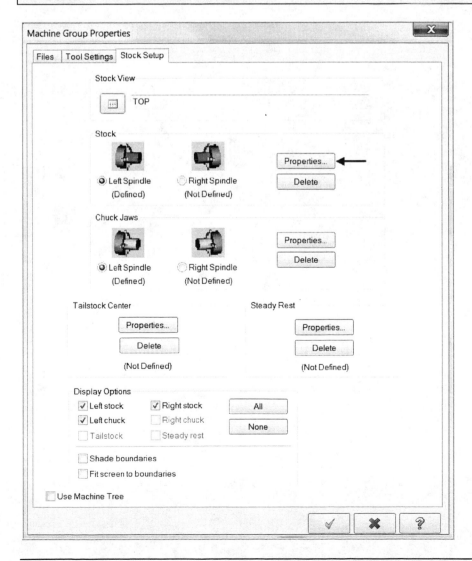

6. In the **Machine Component Manager-Stock** window click on the **Geometry** button and select **Cylinder** as shown below:

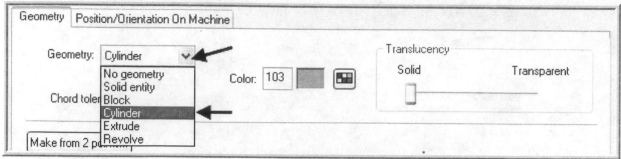

7. In the **Stock setup** set the values as shown below:

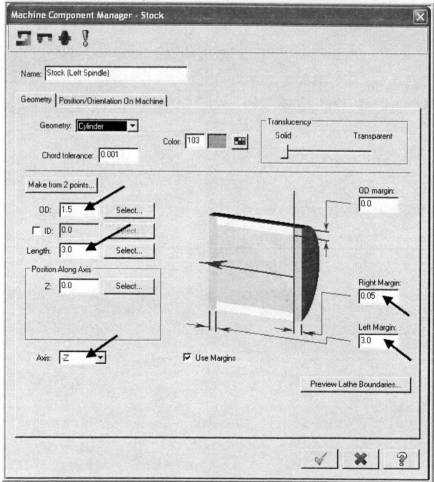

8. Click on the OK icon ☑ to complete this feature.

9. Select the **Chuck Properties** button in the **Stock Setup** page as shown in the screenshot below:

10. In the **Chuck Jaws** setup set the values as shown below:

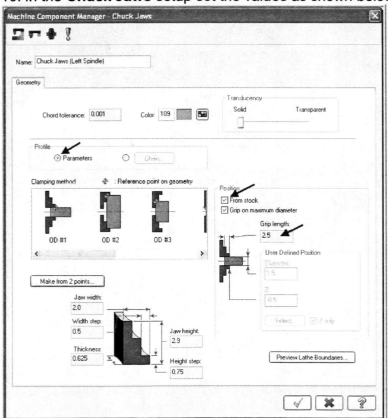

11. Click on the OK icon [✓] to complete this feature.

12. Click on the **Tool Settings** page and make changes as shown below:

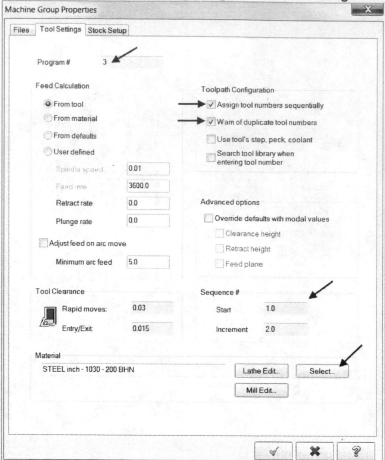

13. To change the **Material** type to Aluminium 6061 click on the **Select** button at the bottom of the Tool Settings page.
14. At the **Material List** dialog box open the Source drop down list and select **Lathe – library.**

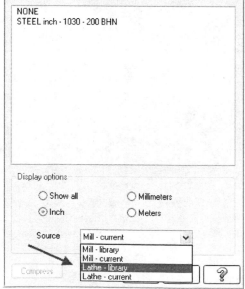

15. From the **Default Materials** list select **ALUMINIUM inch - 6061** and then select .

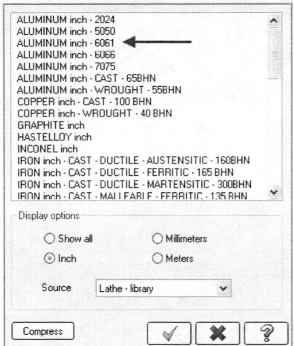

16. Select the OK button ☑ again to complete this Stock Setup function.

17. Zoom out by clicking on the **Un-Zoom previous / .5** icon

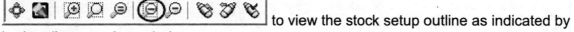 to view the stock setup outline as indicated by broken lines as shown below:

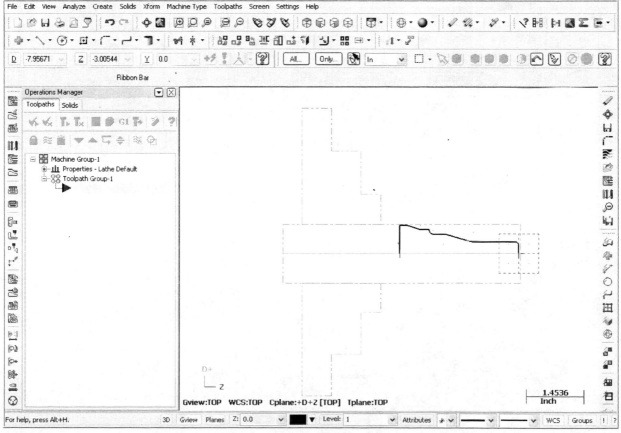

TASK 9:
FACE THE FRONT OF THE PART:
➲ In this task you will use a facing tool to face the front of the part in one cut.

1. Select the **Screen Fit** icon to fit the part to the screen ⊹

2. Then select the **Un-Zoom previous / .5** icon. This function reduces the size of the displayed geometry to 50% of its current size.

3. From the menu bar select **Toolpaths>Face...**

4. When prompted to **"Enter new NC name"** Ensure **Lathe-Lesson-3** is entered as shown below and then select the OK button ✓.

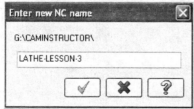

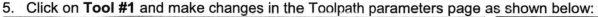

⮑ After selecting the OK button you are confronted with **Toolpath parameters** page. The first task here will be to select **Tool #1 an OD Rough- Right – 80 deg.**

5. Click on **Tool #1** and make changes in the Toolpath parameters page as shown below:

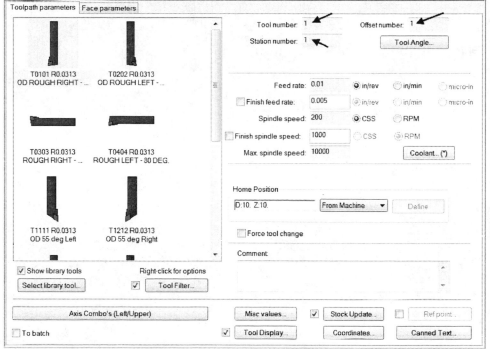

Use the Toolpath parameters tab to: Select a tool, set feeds and speeds, and set other general toolpath parameters.
This tab is very similar for most Lathe toolpaths.

6. Select the **Face parameters** page and make changes as shown below:

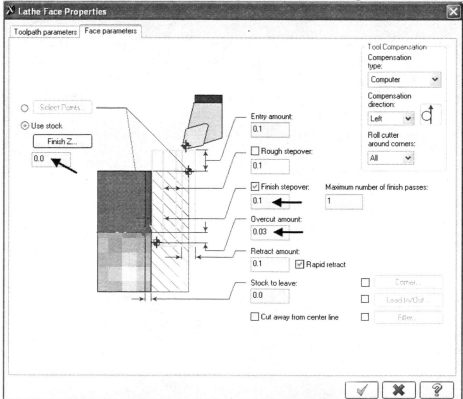

7. Select the OK button [✓] to complete this **Lathe Face** operation.

TASK 10:
ROUGH THE OUTSIDE DIAMETERS
- ⇨ In this task you will use a new Lathe toolpath called Lathe Quick Toolpaths.
- ⇨ In this task you will use the same tool as used for the previous facing operation **Tool #1 an OD Rough- Right – 80 deg.**

1. From the menu bar select **Toolpaths>Quick>Rough...**

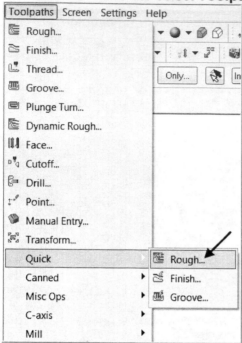

2. In the **Chaining** window chaining mode is set to **Partial** by default.

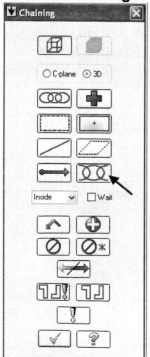

3. Select the chamfer, Line 1 as the start of the **Partial chain**.

> After you have selected the chamfer **ensure** that the arrow is pointing towards the part as shown below. If it is not, select the reverse button in the Chaining dialog box
>
>

4. Then select Line 2 as the end entity in this chain.

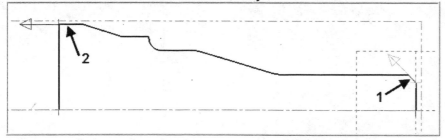

5. Select the OK button [✓] to exit the Chaining dialog window.
6. In the **Toolpath parameters** page select the same tool used to face the part **Tool #1 an OD Rough- Right – 80 deg** and make any necessary changes as shown below:

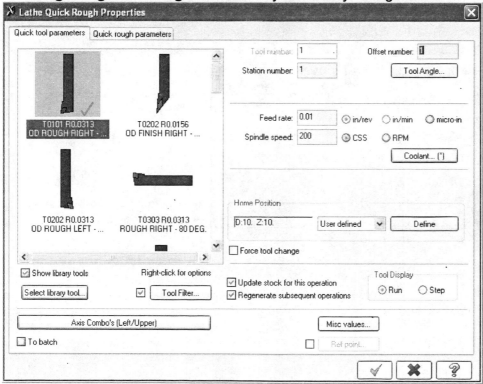

7. Select the **Rough parameters** page and make any necessary changes as shown below:

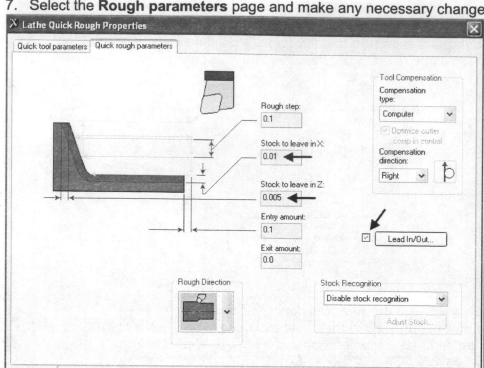

8. Select the **Lead In/Out** button select the **Lead out** page and extend the contour by .2 as shown below:

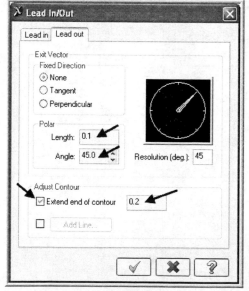

9. Select the OK button [✓] to exit this function.

10. Select the OK button [✓] to exit Rough Parameters.

TASK 11:
FINISH THE OUTSIDE DIAMETERS
⊃ In this task you will finish the outside diameters in one cut using **Tool #2 OD Finish Right – 35 DEG.**

1. From the menu bar select **Toolpaths>Quick>Finish...**

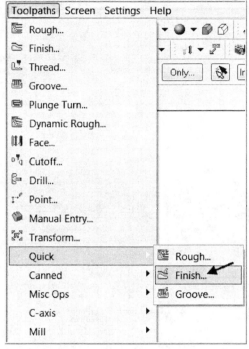

2. Select **Tool #2 OD Finish Right – 35 DEG** tool from the tool list and make any necessary changes as shown below:

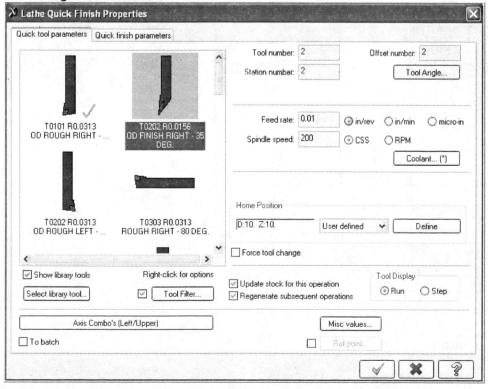

3. Select the **Finish parameters** page and make changes as shown below:

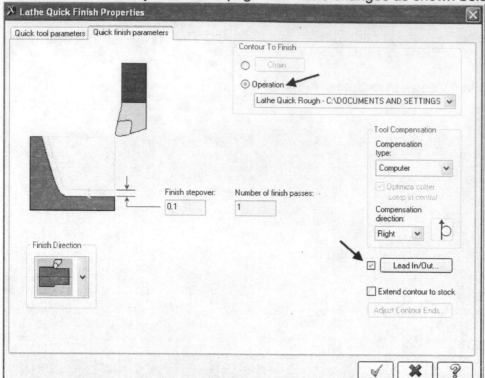

4. Select the **Lead In/Out** button select the **Lead out** page and extend the contour by .2 as shown below:

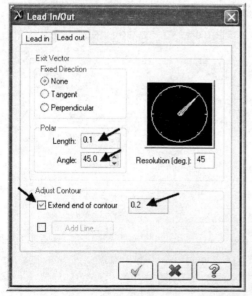

5. Select the OK button [✓] to exit this function.
6. Select the OK button [✓] to exit this function.

TASK 12:
CENTER DRILL THE HOLE

➲ In this task you will center drill .2" depth using **Tool #3 Centre Drill - .25 diameter.**

1. From the menu bar select **Toolpaths>Drill...**

2. Select the **CENTER DRILL .25 DIAMETER** tool from the tool list and make changes as shown below:

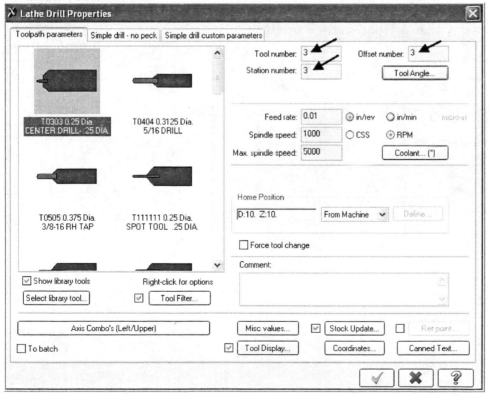

3. Select the **Simple drill – no peck** page and make changes as shown below:

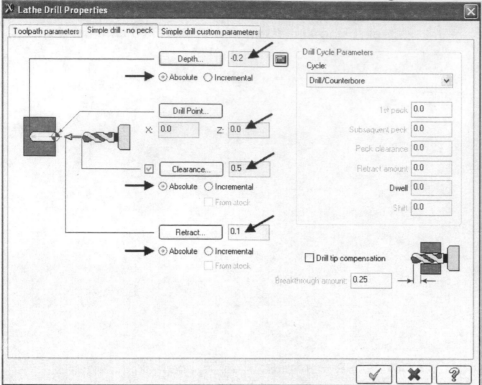

4. Select the OK button [✓] to exit **Simple drill – no peck.**

TASK 13:
TAP DRILL THE 5/16" HOLE

➲ In this task you will drill the 5/16" hole .75" depth using a **0.3125 (5/16") Drill.**

1. From the menu bar select **Toolpaths> Drill...**

2. Click on the **Select library tool...** button in the lower left corner of the Toolpath parameters page as shown below:

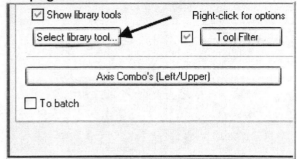

3. At the top left of this dialog box open up the Select new folder icon  to show the library tools list and select **LDRILLS.**

4. Scroll down and select the **0.3125 Dia. 5/16" DRILL** from the list.

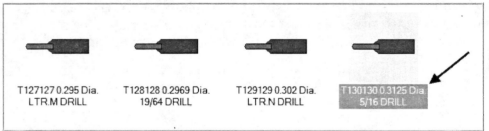

5. Select the OK button ✓.

6. Ensure settings are as shown below:

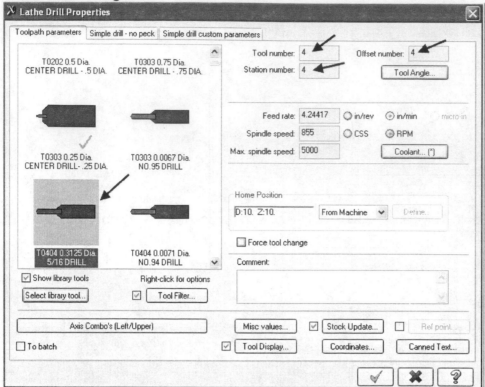

7. Select the **Simple drill – no peck** page and make changes as shown below. This hole will be **peck drilled**. The **depth of the hole is 1.00" from the front face** so click in the space for depth and type in **-1.0** and hit the tab key, Mastercam figures out the value for you. Make changes as shown below:

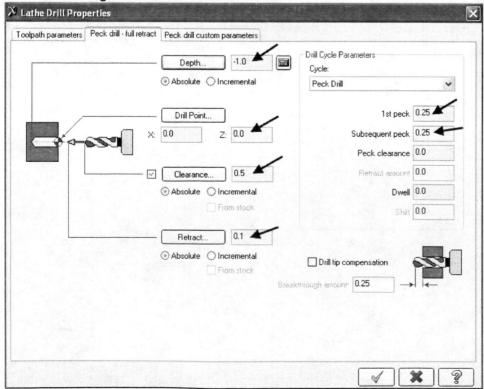

The hole depth on the drawing is dimensioned to .a depth of 1.0" at the full diameter of the hole. So the point of the drill will have to go deeper than 1.0"
You can use the depth calculator button to figure out the correct depth.

8. Select the **Depth Calculator** icon.

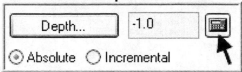

9. Make changes to the **Depth Calculator** as shown below:

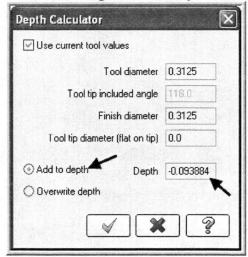

10. Select the OK button to exit **the Depth Calculator.**
11. The depth has now been updated.

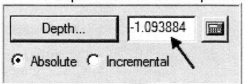

12. Select the OK button to exit **Peck drill – full retract.**

TASK 14:
TAP 3/8" – 16 UNC
➲ In this task you will tap the 3/8"-16 hole 1" deep.

1. From the menu bar select **Toolpaths>Drill…**

2. Click on the **Select library tool…** button in the lower left corner of the Toolpath parameters page as shown below:

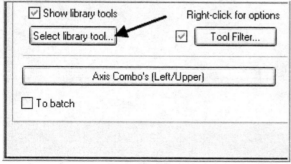

3. Select the **select new folder** icon  at the top of the dialog box and then the **LTAPS** from the list as shown below:

4. Select the OK button ✓ after selecting **LTAPS**.

5. Scroll down and select **the 0.375 Dia. 3/8"-16 RH TAP** from the list.
6. Select the OK button ✓.
7. Ensure necessary settings are as shown below:

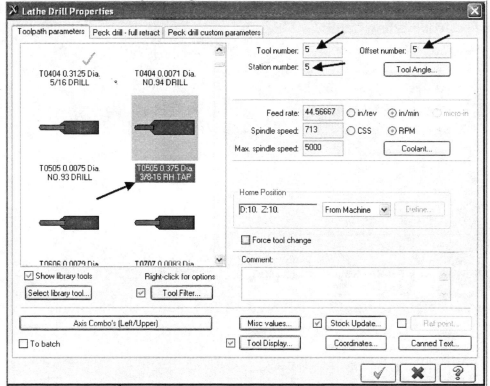

8. Select the **Peck drill – full retract** page and make changes to tap as shown below:

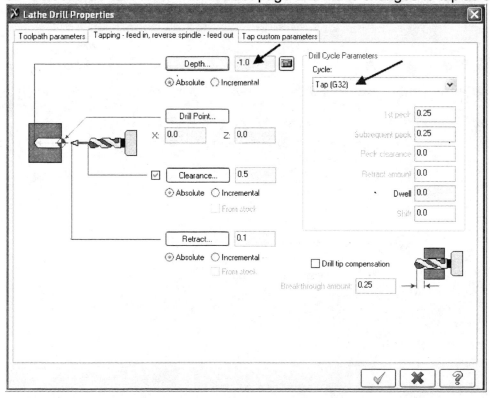

9. Select the OK button ✓ to exit **Tapping – feed in, reverse spindle – feed out.**

TASK 15:
CUT OFF THE PART
➲ In this task you will finish the outside diameters in one cut using **Tool #6 Cutoff Right Width .125.**

1. From the menu bar select **Toolpaths> Cutoff...**

2. Select the **Alt key** and the **T** key on the keyboard to hide the toolpath lines.

Toolpath Lines visible: **Press Alt T to hide toolpath Lines:**

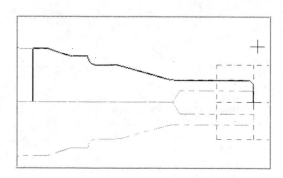

3. Pick where **Line 8 and Line 9** meet as shown below: (Move the cursor over the corner until

the visual cue 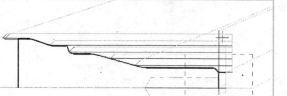 for End point displays and then click on this point.)

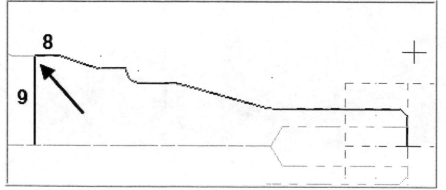

4. Click on the **Select library tool...** button.

5. Select the **select new folder** icon  at the top of the dialog box and then the
   Lathe_Inch from the list as shown below:

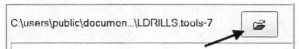

C:\users\public\documen...\LDRILLS.tools-7

6. Select the OK button after selecting **Lathe_Inch**.
7. Scroll down and select **OD Cutoff Right Width .125** from the list.
8. Select the OK button.
9. Make changes as shown below in the **Toolpath parameters** page.

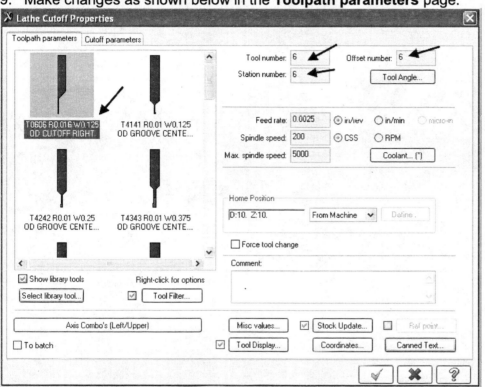

10. Select the **Cutoff parameters** page and make sure the settings are as shown below:

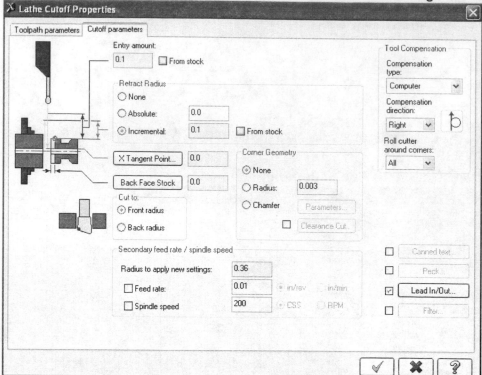

11. Select the OK button to exit **Cutoff parameters.**

TASK 16:
VERIFY THE TOOLPATH

➲ Mastercam's Verify utility allows you to use solid models to simulate the machining of a part. The model created by the verification represents the surface finish, and shows collisions, if any exist.

1. In the Toolpath Manager pick all the operations to backplot by picking the **Select All** icon 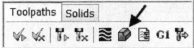 .

2. Select the **Verify selected operations** icon shown below:

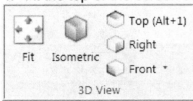

3. **Maximize** the Backplot/Verify window if required.
4. At the top of the screen select the **Isometric** icon and then select **Fit**.

		Top (Alt+1)
		Right
Fit	Isometric	Front ▾
	3D View	

5. Activate the options shown below in the **Visibility** section of the Home tab. **Initial Stock not** activated.

☐ Toolpath	✔ Stock
✔ Tool	☐ Initial Stock
☐ Workpiece	✔ Fixtures
Visibility	

6. Activate the **Color Loop** to change the color of the tools for the verified part.

Color Loop

7. In the lower right corner of the screen now set the run **Speed** to slow by moving the slider bar pointer over to the left as shown below.

Speed:

8. Now select the **Play Simulation** button to review the toolpaths.

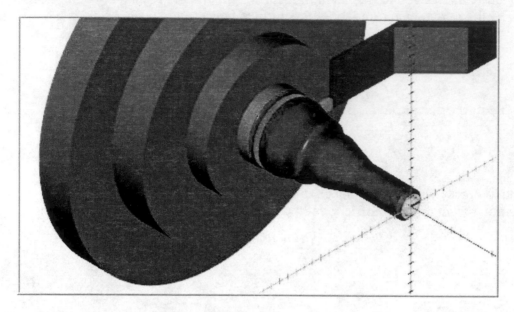

9. Select the **Close** button in the top right hand corner to exit Verify.

TASK 17:
SAVE THE UPDATED MASTERCAM FILE

1. Select the save icon from the toolbar

TASK 18:
POST AND CREATE THE CNC CODE FILE

1. Ensure all the operations are selected by picking the **Select All** icon  from the Toolpaths manager.

2. Select the **Post selected operations** button from the Toolpaths manager.
➲ **Please Note:** If you cannot see **G1** click on the right pane of the Toolpaths manager window and expand the window to the right.

3. In the Post processing window, make the necessary changes as shown below:

About Post Processing

NC file:
Select this option to save the NC file. The file name and extension are stored in the machine group properties for the selected operation. If you are posting operations from different machine groups or Mastercam files, or batch processing, Mastercam will create several files according to the settings for each machine group.

Edit:
When checked, automatically launches the default text editor with the file displayed so that you can review or modify it.

4. Select the OK button to continue.

5. Ensure the same name as your Mastercam part file name is displayed in the **NC File name** field as shown below:

File name: LATHE-LESSON-3

Save as type: NC Files (*.NC)

6. Select the **Save** button.
7. The CNC code file opens up in the default editor.

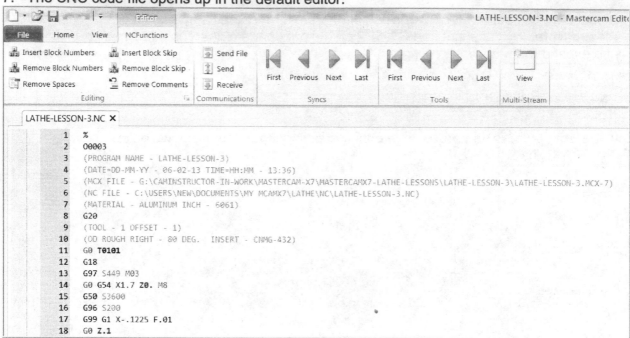

8. Select the ⊠ in the top right corner to exit the CNC editor.

9. This completes LATHE-LESSON-3.

LATHE-LESSON-3 EXERCISE

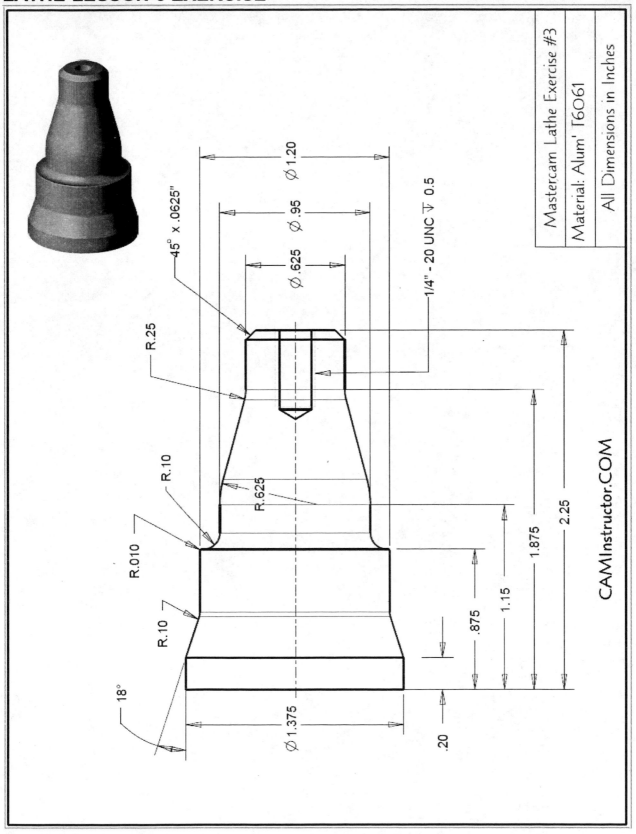

Mastercam Lathe Exercise #3

Material: Alum' T6061

All Dimensions in Inches

⌀ 1.20

⌀ .95

⌀ .625

45° x .0625"

1/4" - 20 UNC ⎁ 0.5

R.25

R.10

R.625

R.010

R.10

18°

⌀ 1.375

.20

.875

1.15

1.875

2.25

CAMInstructor.COM

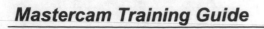

Mastercam. X⁷
Training
Guide

Lathe-Lesson-4
Face, Rough, Finish, Groove,
Thread and Cutoff

camInstructor

Objectives

You will create the geometry for Lathe Lesson 2, and then generate a toolpath to machine the part on a CNC lathe. This lesson covers the following topics:

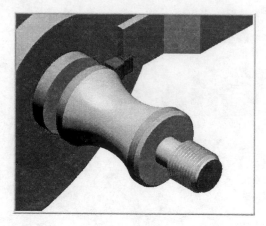

➲ **Create a 2-dimensional drawing by:**
Creating lines.
Creating fillets.
Creating chamfers.

➲ **Establish Stock and Chuck Setup settings:**
Stock size.
Chuck Configuration.
Material for the part.
Feed calculation.

➲ **Generate a 2-dimensional lathe toolpath
  consisting of:**
Lathe Face.
Lathe Rough.
Lathe Finish.
Lathe Groove.
Lathe Thread.
Lathe Cutoff.

➲ **Inspect the toolpath using Mastercam's Verify and Backplot by:**
Launching the Verify function to machine the part on the screen.
Generating the NC- code.

LATHE - LESSON - 4 DRAWING

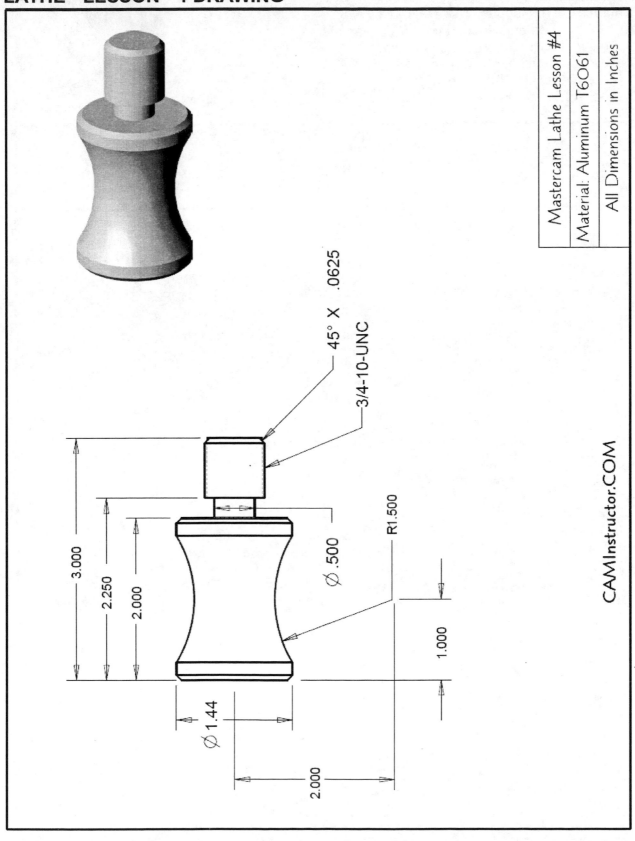

Mastercam Lathe Lesson #4

Material: Aluminum T6061

All Dimensions in Inches

45° X .0625

3/4-10-UNC

3.000

2.250

2.000

Ø .500

R1.500

1.000

Ø 1.44

2.000

CAMInstructor.COM

TOOL LIST

Five tools will be used to create this part.
- ➲ Tool #1 Face and Rough the outside diameters
- ➲ Tool #2 Finish the outside diameters
- ➲ Tool #3 Machine the Groove
- ➲ Tool #4 Machine the Thread
- ➲ Tool #5 Cutoff the part

```
            Tool List of LATHE-LESSON-4.MCX-5

Proj./Part No.: 0                    Date        : 06/22/10
Drawing No.   : 1                    Customer    : -
Prog. No.     : 4                    Programmer  : 1
```

```
          Tool type      : T0101: specific tool type - OD ROUGH RIGHT - 80 DEG.
          Manufact.code  :
          Holder/Insert  : DCGNR-164D / CNMG-432
          Setup length   :
          Spindle RPM    :     200    Feedrate UPR :     0.01    Corner radius :    0.0313
          Length offset  :       1    Tool chan. D,Z:   14   ,     8


          Tool type      : T0202: specific tool type - OD FINISH RIGHT - 35 DEG.
          Manufact.code  :
          Holder/Insert  : MVJNR-164D / VNMG-431
          Setup length   :
          Spindle RPM    :     200    Feedrate UPR :     0.01    Corner radius :    0.0156
          Length offset  :       2    Tool chan. D,Z:   14   ,     8


          Tool type      : T0303: specific tool type - OD GROOVE RIGHT - NARROW
          Manufact.code  :
          Holder/Insert  : / GC-4125
          Setup length   :
          Spindle RPM    :     200    Feedrate UPM :     20     Corner radius :    0.01
          Length offset  :       3    Tool chan. D,Z:   14   ,     8


          Tool type      : T0404: specific tool type - OD THREAD RIGHT
          Manufact.code  :
          Holder/Insert  : /
          Setup length   :
          Spindle RPM    :     200    Feedrate UPM :     20     Corner radius :    0.0144
          Length offset  :       4    Tool chan. D,Z:   14   ,     8


          Tool type      : T0505: specific tool type - Lathe Tool 75
          Manufact.code  :
          Holder/Insert  : MVJNR-164D / VNMG-431
          Setup length   :
          Spindle RPM    :     200    Feedrate UPR :     0.01    Corner radius :    0.0156
          Length offset  :       5    Tool chan. D,Z:   14   ,     8
```

LESSON - 4 - THE PROCESS

Geometry Creation

TASK 1:   Setting the Environment
TASK 2:   Setting the Construction Planes
TASK 3:   Create the Geometry
TASK 4:   Create the 1.5" Radius
TASK 5:   Create the Chamfers
TASK 6:   Save the Drawing

Toolpath Creation

TASK 7:   Define the Stock and Chuck Parameters
TASK 8:   Face the Front of the Part
TASK 9:   Rough the Outside Diameters
TASK 10:   Finish the Outside Diameters
TASK 11:   Cut the Groove
TASK 12:   Cut the Thread
TASK 13:   Finish the Radius
TASK 14:   Cut off the Part
TASK 15:   Verify the toolpath
TASK 16:   Save the updated Mastercam file
TASK 17:   Post and create the CNC code file

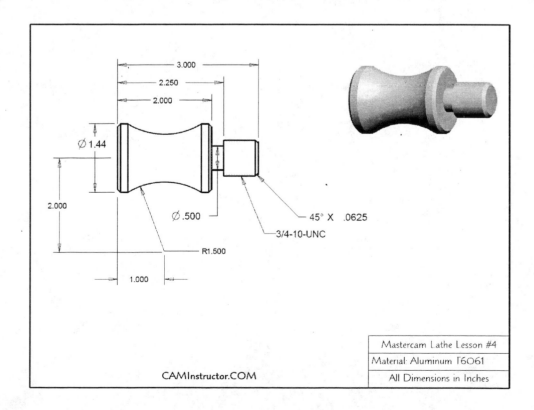

3.000
2.250
2.000
∅ 1.44
2.000
∅ .500
45° X .0625
3/4-10-UNC
R1.500
1.000

CAMInstructor.COM

| Mastercam Lathe Lesson #4 |
| Material: Aluminum T6061 |
| All Dimensions in Inches |

Geometry Creation

TASK 1:
SETTING THE ENVIRONMENT

Before starting the geometry creation you should set up the grid and toolbars as outlined in the **Setting the Environment** section at the beginning of this text:
1. Set up the Grid. This will help identify the location of the origin.
2. Customize the toolbars to machine a part on the Lathe.
3. Set the machine type to the default Lathe.

TASK 2:
SETTING THE CONSTRUCTION PLANES:

⊃ **Set the Construction Plane to Lathe diameter +D +Z (WCS)**
1. Click on Planes at the bottom of the screen as shown below:

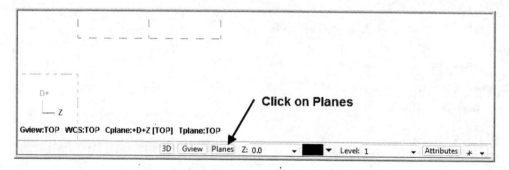

2. Click on Lathe diameter>+D +Z (WCS) as shown below:

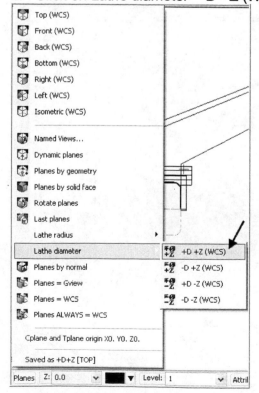

TASK 3:
CREATE THE GEOMETRY

➲ This task explains how to create the geometry of this part. In this lathe part you only need to create **half of the geometry,** the geometry above the center line.

➲ Lines 1 through 7 will be created first and then the radius and chamfer will be created.

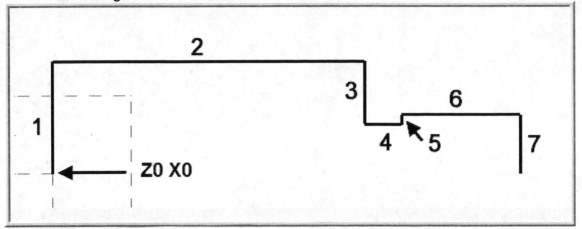

➲ **Create Line #1**

1. Select from the pull down menu **Create>Line>Endpoint...**

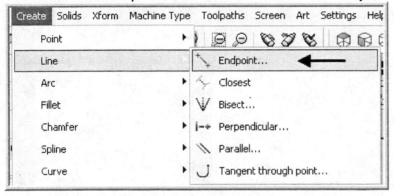

2. The Line ribbon bar appears:

3. Move the cursor over the **center of the grid** and as you get close to the origin a visual cue appears. This is the cue that will allow you to snap to the **origin**. With this visual cue highlighted pick the **origin**.

AutoCursor: Visual Cues detects and highlights endpoints and midpoints of curves, lines, arc center points, and point entities. In addition, AutoCursor can snap to angle, nearest, tangent, perpendicular, horizontal, and vertical conditions.

➲ The following are Mastercam Visual Cues:

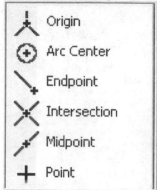
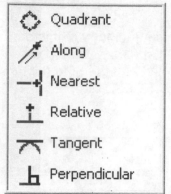

4. You are next prompted to **"Specify the second endpoint"**. On the left hand side of the Line ribbon bar click on the **Multi-Line** button to activate it as shown below by the arrow:

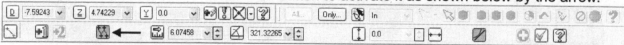

5. Click in the **D** value space (Diameter) (as shown by the arrow below) and enter a value of **1.44**. Hit the Enter key and enter a value of **0 for the Z**, hit the Enter key again and enter a value of **0 for the Y** and hit Enter.

6. A vertical line should be visible as shown below:

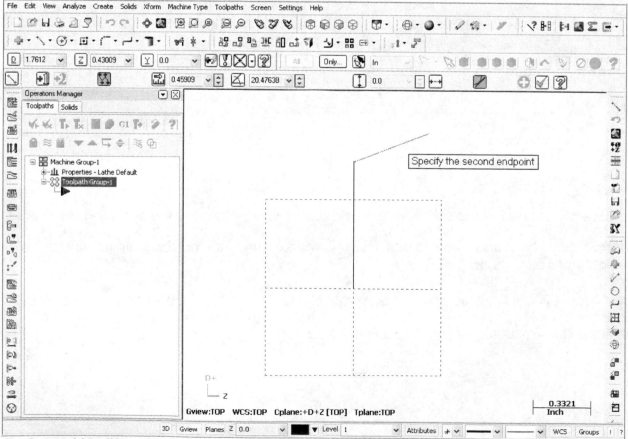

➲ Create Line #2

7. **"Specify the second endpoint"**; Type in **1.44 in D** hit Enter, type in **2.0 in Z** and hit Enter and type in **0.0 in Y** and hit Enter.

D	1.44	⌄	Z	2.0	⌄	Y	0.0	⌄

➲ **Create Line #3**
8. **"Specify the second endpoint"**; Type in **.625 in D** hit Enter, type in **2.0 in Z** and hit Enter and type in **0.0 in Y** and hit Enter.

D	.625	⌄	Z	2.0	⌄	Y	0.0	⌄

➲ **Create Line #4**
9. **"Specify the second endpoint"**; Type in **.625 in D** hit Enter, type in **2.250 in Z** and hit Enter and type in **0.0 in Y** and hit Enter.

D	.625	⌄	Z	2.250	⌄	Y	0.0	⌄

10. Fit the image to the screen by clicking on the **Fit** icon as shown below:

11. Then unzoom by clicking on the **Un-Zoom Previous / .5** icon as shown below:

➲ **Create Line #5**
12. **"Specify the second endpoint"**; Type in **.75 in D** hit Enter, type in **2.250 in Z** and hit Enter and type in **0.0 in Y** and hit Enter.

D	.75	⌄	Z	2.250	⌄	Y	0.0	⌄

➲ **Create Line #6**
13. **"Specify the second endpoint"**; Type in **0.75 in D** hit Enter, type in **3.0 in Z** and hit Enter and type in **0.0 in Y** and hit Enter.

D	.75	⌄	Z	3.00	⌄	Y	0.0	⌄

➲ **Create Line #7**
14. **"Specify the second endpoint"**; Type in **0.0 in D** hit Enter, type in **3.0 in Z** and hit Enter and type in **0.0 in Y** and hit Enter.

D	0.0	⌄	Z	3.00	⌄	Y	0.0	⌄

15. Click on the **OK** icon to complete this feature.

16. Select the **Screen Fit** icon to fit the part to the screen.

17. Your geometry should look like the figure below.

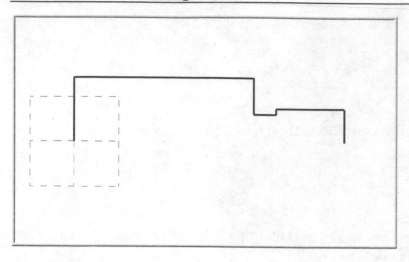

TASK 4:
CREATE THE 1.5" RADIUS

➲ **Create the Arc Center Point.**

1. Select **Create>Point>Dynamic...**

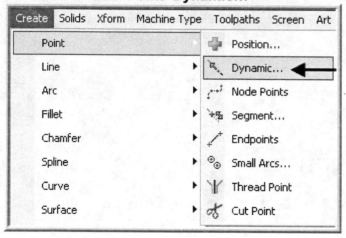

2. The **Create Point Dynamic** ribbon bar appears and you are prompted to;

Select line, arc, spline, surface, or solid face

3. Select **line 1** below the half way point as shown below:

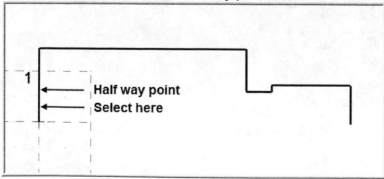

4. Click in the space of the distance window and enter **2.0** and hit the tab key.

5. Enter **1.0** in the **offset** window and hit the tab key.

6. Click on OK ☑.
7. Click on OK ☑.
8. **Fit** the image to the screen ✥.
9. A point will be created as shown in the image below:

+ ⟵ **New Point**

➲ **Create the 1.5" Arc**

10. Select **Create>Arc>Circle Center Point...**

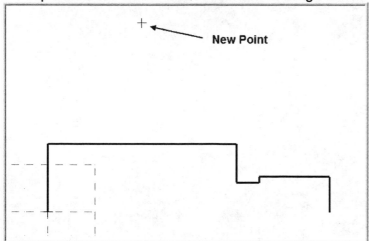

11. The **Create Circle** ribbon bar appears and you are prompted to ⌈Enter the center point⌉.
12. Click on the newly created point.
13. Click in the **Radius** window and type **1.5** as shown below and hit the **enter** key:

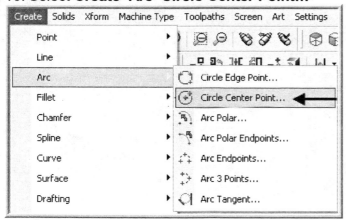

14. Click on OK ☑.

15. An Arc is created as shown below:

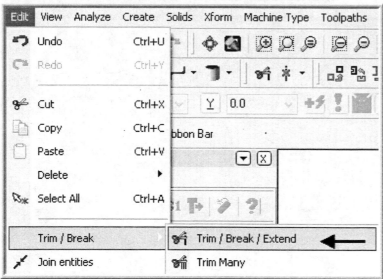

➲ **Trim the Arc**

16. Select **Edit>Trim/Break>Trim/Break/Extend…**

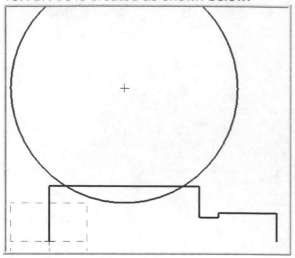

17. **The Trim/Break** ribbon bar appears and you are prompted to | Select the entity to trim/extend |.

18. Click on the **Divide** Button as shown below:

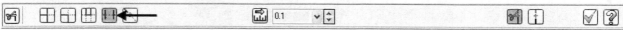

19. **Fit** the image to the screen [⬥] .

20. You are prompted to | Select the curve to divide |.

21. Click on the entities you DO NOT want to keep; **Entity 1, Entity 2 and Entity 3** as shown below:

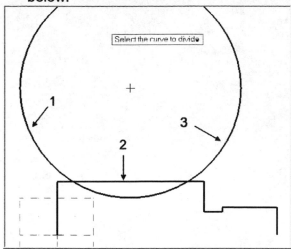

22. Click on OK 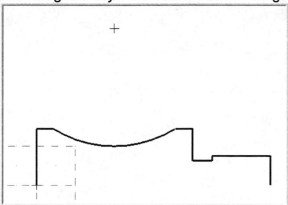.

23. The geometry should look like the image below:

➲ **Delete the Point**

24. Select the point shown above. It should change color.
25. Hit the **Delete** key.

26. **Fit** to Screen

TASK 5:
CREATE THE CHAMFERS

➲ **Create 3 Chamfers 45 degrees x .0625.**

1. Select **Create>Chamfer>Entities...**

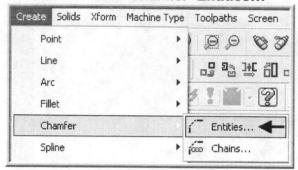

2. You are prompted to |Select line or arc|.
3. Click in the Distance window as shown below and type in **.0625** and hit enter:

4. Ensure the **1 Distance** option is selected as shown below:

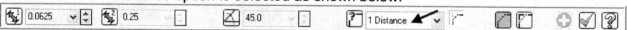

5. Click on **line 1** and then **line 2** as shown below:

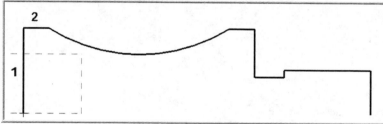

6. Click on **Apply** .
7. Click on **line 3** and then **line 4** as shown below:

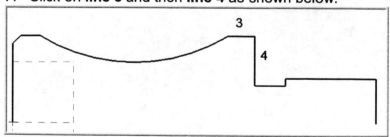

8. Click on **Apply** .

9. Click on **line 5** and then **line 6** as shown below:

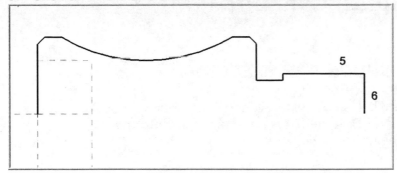

10. Click on OK ✓.
11. The completed geometry should look like the image below:

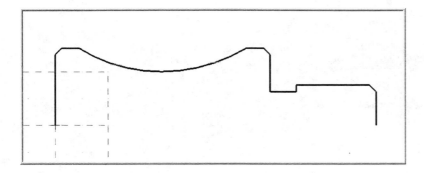

TASK 6:
SAVE THE DRAWING

1. Select **File.**
2. Select **Save as.**
3. In the **"File name"** box, type **"Lathe-Lesson-4".**
4. Save to an appropriate location.
5. Select the Save button to save the file and complete this function.

| File name: | LATHE-LESSON-4 | ▼ |
| Save as type: | Mastercam X7 Files (*.MCX-7) | ▼ |

Toolpath Creation

TASK 7:
DEFINING THE STOCK AND CHUCK PARAMETERS

1. Ensure your screen looks like the image below:
   a. The Toolpaths Manager is open, if it is not Select Alt and O on your keyboard to open it.
   b. The properties icon displays **Lathe Default**. If it is not refer to **Setting the Environment** chapter at the beginning of the book.
   c. The **Lathe Lesson-4** Geometry is showing.
2. Select the screen fit icon as shown to the right to display the geometry:

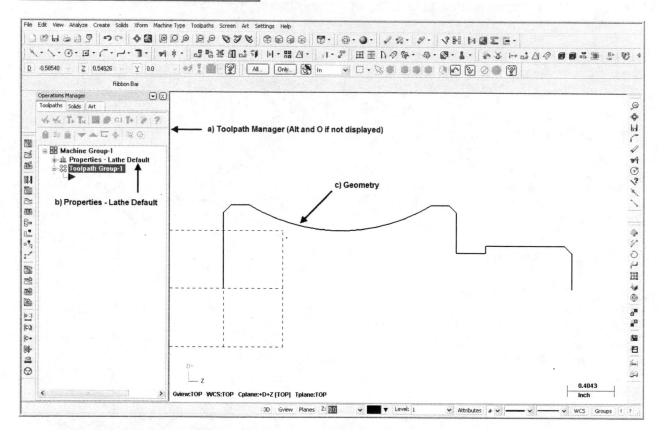

3. Select the plus in front of **Properties** to expand the Machine Group Properties.

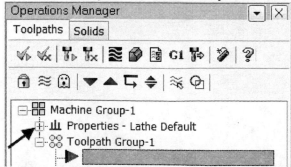

4. Select **Stock setup** in the Toolpaths Manager window.

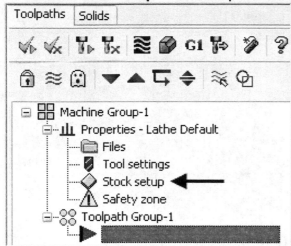

5. Select the **Stock Properties** button in the **Stock Setup** page as shown in the screenshot below:

➲ Note: To learn how to complete this section of the **Stock Setup** refer to the **Tips and Techniques** section on the **Mastercam Training Guide – Lathe CD** that accompanies this book.

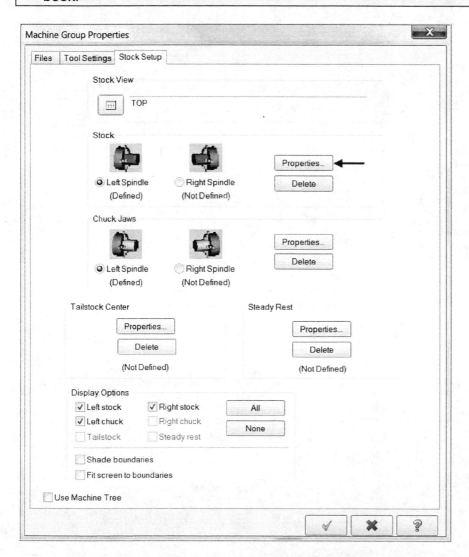

6. In the **Machine Component Manager-Stock** window click on the **Geometry** button and select **Cylinder** as shown below:

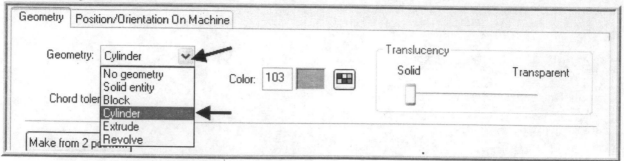

7. In the **Stock setup** set the values as shown below:

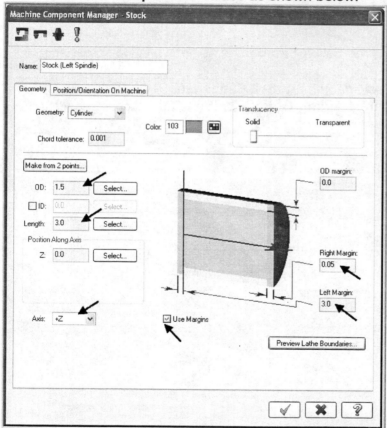

8. Click on the OK icon [✓] to complete this feature.

9. Select the **Chuck Properties** button in the **Stock Setup** page as shown in the screenshot below:

10. In the **Chuck Jaws** setup set the values as shown below:

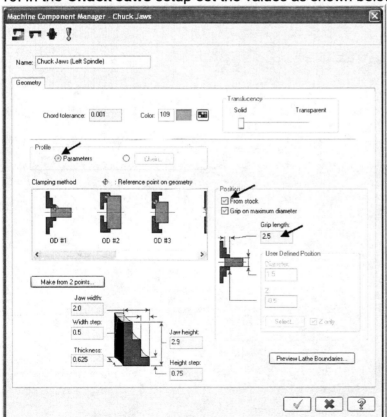

11. Click on the OK icon ✓ to complete this feature.

12. Click on the **Tool Settings** page and make changes as shown below:

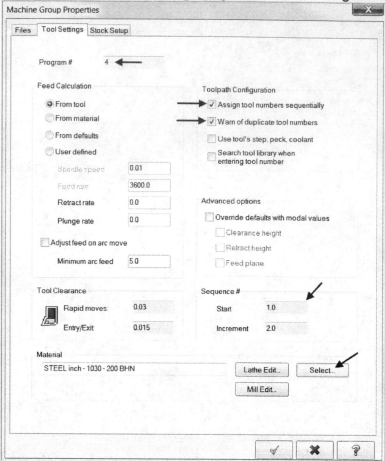

13. To change the **Material** type to Aluminium 6061 pick the **Select** button at the bottom of the Tool Settings page.

14. At the **Material List** dialog box open the Source drop down list and select **Lathe – library.**

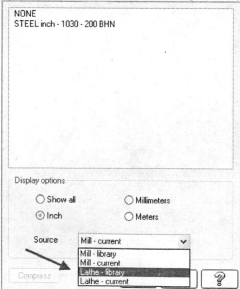

15. From the **Default Materials** list select **ALUMINIUM inch - 6061** and then select .

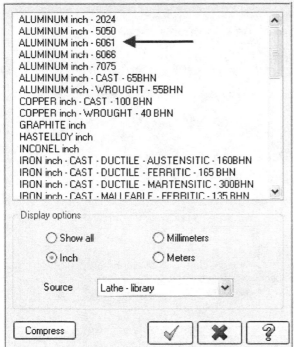

16. Select the OK button ✓ again to complete this **Stock Setup** function.

17. Zoom out by clicking on the **Un-Zoom Previous / .5** icon

to view the stock setup outline as indicated by broken lines as shown below:

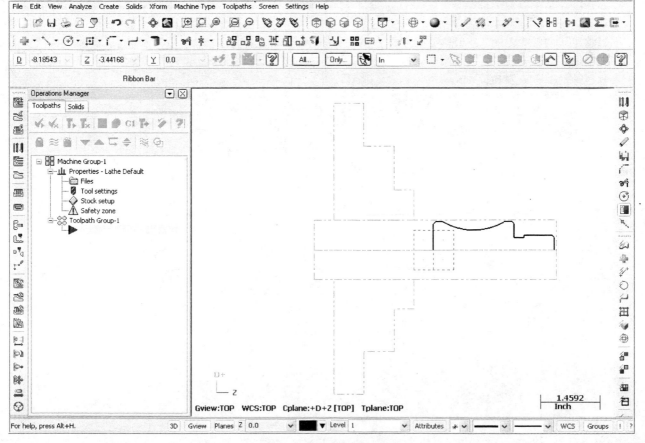

TASK 8:
FACE THE FRONT OF THE PART:

➲ In this task you will use a facing tool to face the front of the part in one cut.

1. Select the **Screen Fit** icon to fit the part to the screen ⊕.

2. Then select the **Un-Zoom previous / .5** icon. This function reduces the size of the displayed geometry to 50% of its current size.

3. From the menu bar select **Toolpaths>Face...**

4. When prompted to **"Enter new NC name"** Ensure **LATHE-LESSON-4** is entered as shown below and then select the OK button ✓.

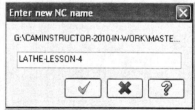

⊃ After selecting the OK button you are confronted with **Toolpath parameters** page. The first task here will be to select **Tool #1 a Roughing – 80 deg.**

5. Click on **Tool 0101 Roughing – 80 degree** and ensure the settings are the same as in the Toolpath parameters page as shown below:

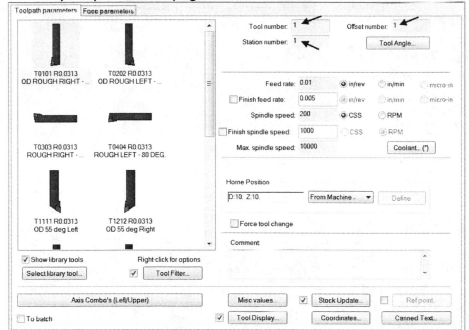

Use the Toolpath parameters tab to: Select a tool, set feeds and speeds, and set other general toolpath parameters.
This tab is very similar for most Lathe toolpaths.

6. Select the **Face parameters** page and make changes as shown below:

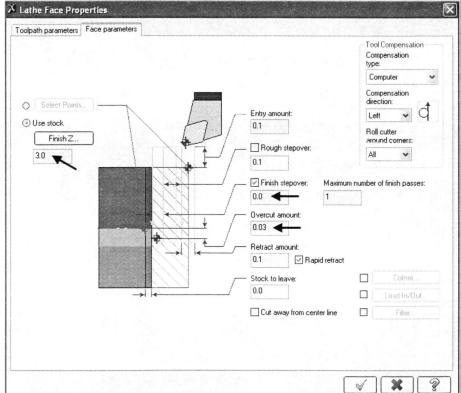

7. Select the OK button ✓ to complete this **Lathe Face** operation.

TASK 9:
ROUGH THE OUTSIDE DIAMETERS
⮞ In this task you will use a Lathe toolpath called Lathe Quick Toolpaths.
⮞ In this task you will use the same tool as used for the previous facing operation **Tool #1 an OD Rough- Right – 80 deg.**

1. From the menu bar select **Toolpaths>Quick>Rough ...**

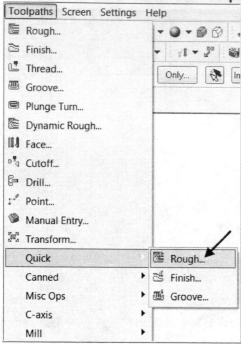

2. In the **Chaining** window Chaining mode is set to **Partial** by default.

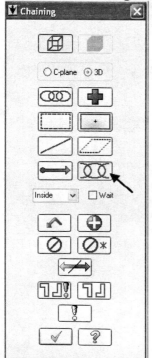

3. Select the chamfer, Line 1 as the start of the **Partial chain**.

After you have selected the chamfer **ensure** that the arrow is pointing towards the part as shown below. If it is not select the reverse button in the Chaining dialog box

4. Then select the chamfer, Line 2 as the end entity in this chain.

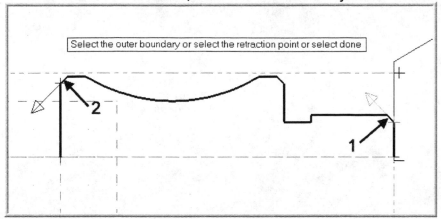

5. Select the OK button to exit the Chaining dialog window.
6. In the **Quick tool parameters** page select the **Tool #1 an Roughing – 80 deg** and make any necessary changes as shown below:

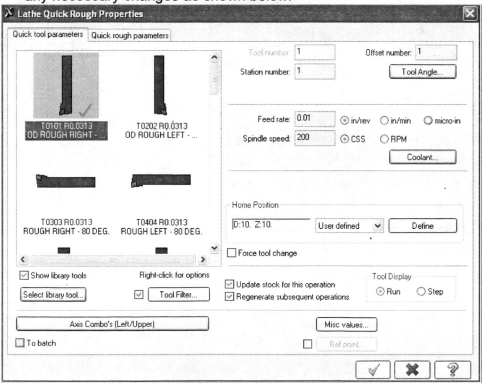

7. Select the **Quick Rough parameters** page and make any necessary changes as shown below:

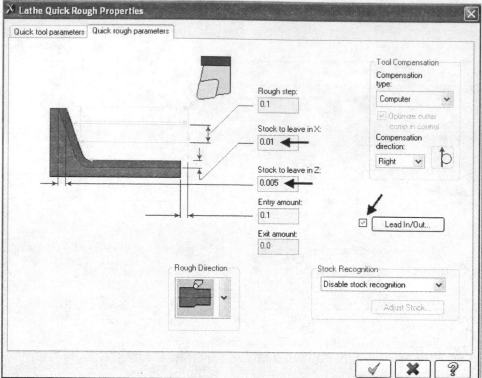

8. Select the OK button to exit Rough Parameters.

TASK 10:
FINISH THE DIAMETER

➲ In this task you will finish the diameter using **Tool #2 OD Finish Right – 35 DEG.**

1. From the menu bar select **Toolpaths>Quick>Finish...**

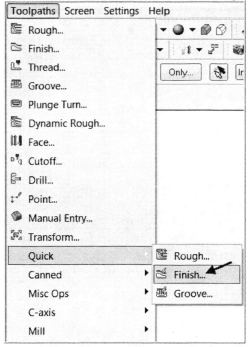

2. Select **Tool #2 OD Finish Right – 35 DEG** tool from the tool list and make any necessary changes as shown below:

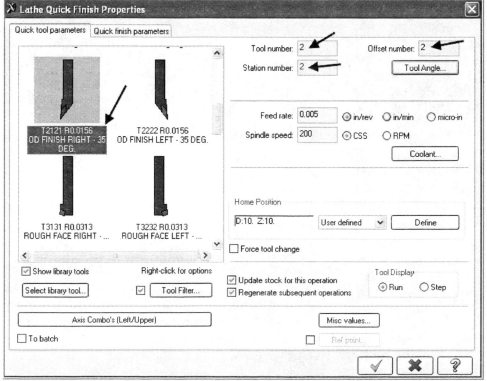

3. Click on the **Quick finish parameters** page and make changes as shown below:

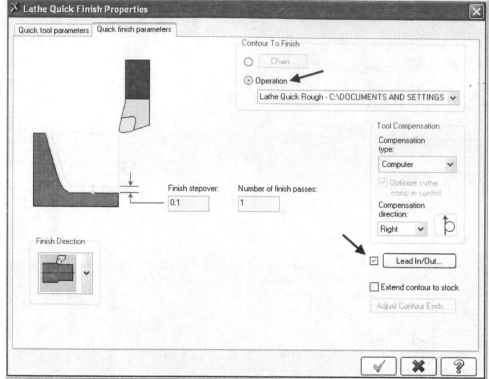

4. Click on the **Lead In/Out** button.
5. Make the necessary changes as shown below on the **Lead in** page. In order to adjust the **dial (#1),** click on the desired location of the arrow:

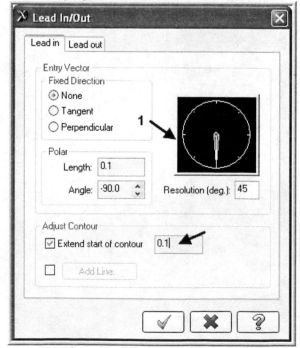

6. Select the OK button ☑ to exit the **Lead In/Out** window.
7. Select the OK button ☑ to exit the **Lathe Quick Finish** parameters.

TASK 11:
CUT THE GROOVE

➲ In this task you will use the Lathe Groove toolpath using **Tool #3 OD Groove Right Width .125.**

1. From the menu bar select **Toolpaths>Groove...**

2. The **Grooving Options** window appears. Click on the 2 Points option as shown below:

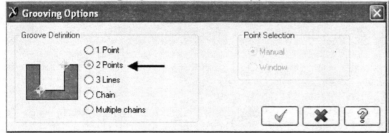

The **2 Points Groove Definition** will enable you to pick 2 points of the groove to define the groove.

---

3. Click on OK ☑.
4. **Alt and T** on the keyboard to hide the toolpath.
5. Click on the **2 points** as shown below:

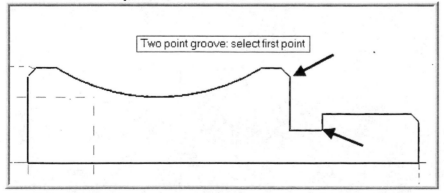

Two point groove: select first point

6. Hit **Enter**.

7. Select **Tool #3 OD Groove Right Width .125** tool from the tool list and make any necessary changes as shown below:

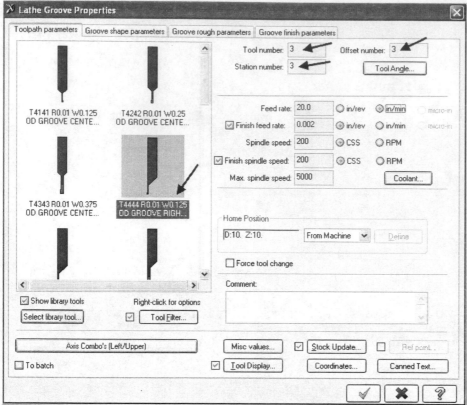

8. Click on the **Groove shape parameters** and take note of the settings. No changes will need to be made:

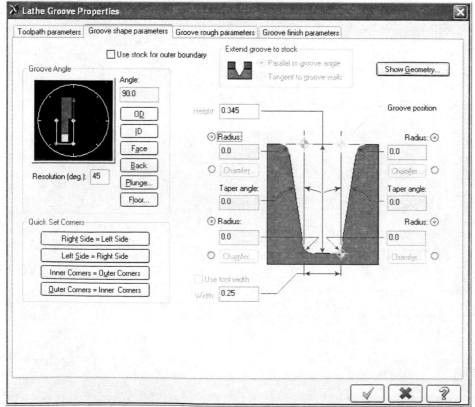

9. Click on the **Groove rough parameters** and take note of the settings. No changes will need to be made:

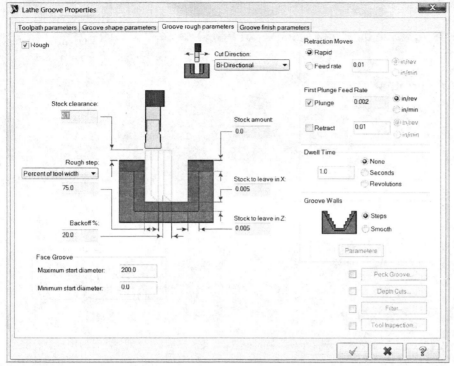

10. Click on the **Groove finish parameters** and take note of the settings. No changes will need to be made:

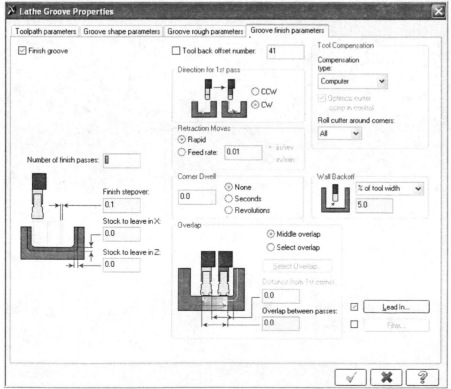

11. Click on OK ✓ .

TASK 12:
THREAD THE PART

➲ In this task you will thread the outside diameter using **Tool #4 R0.0144 OD THREAD RIGHT.**

1. From the menu bar select **Toolpaths>Thread...**

2. Scroll down the tool window if necessary and select the **Tool #4 R0.0144 OD THREAD RIGHT** tool and make changes as shown below in the **Toolpath parameters** page.

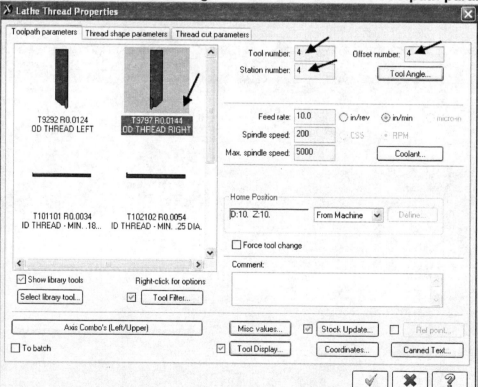

3. Click on the **Thread shape parameters** tab.

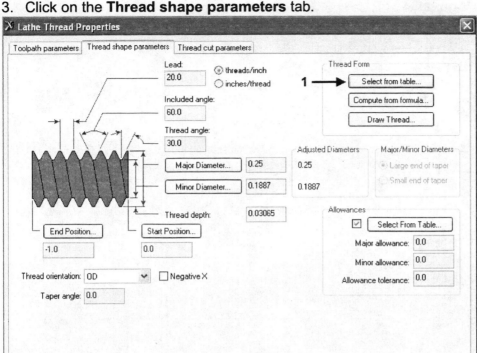

4. Click on **Select from table** (1) as shown above:
5. Click on the **Thread forms** button (1) and select **Unified – UNC, UNF** (2) as shown below:

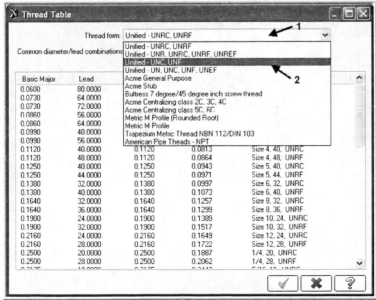

6. Scroll down and click on the **0.7500 10.000 (3/4, 10. UNC)** thread as shown below:

0.6250	11.0000	0.6250	0.5266	5/8, 11, UNC
0.6250	18.0000	0.6250	0.5649	5/8, 18, UNF
0.7500	10.0000	0.7500	0.6417	3/4, 10, UNC
0.7500	16.0000	0.7500	0.6823	3/4, 16, UNF
0.8750	9.0000	0.8750	0.7547	7/8, 9, UNC

7. Click on OK.

8. Click on the **Start Position** button (1) as shown below:

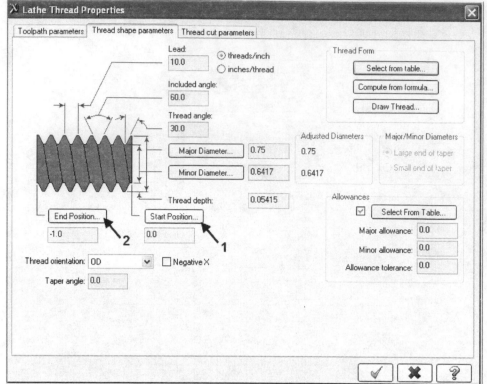

9. Click on the point as shown below:

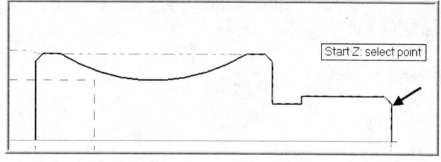

Start Z: select point

10. Click on the **End Position** button (2) as shown in step 8.
11. Click on the point as shown below:

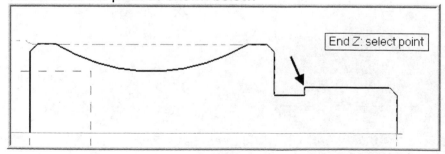

End Z: select point

12. Your Start and End Positions should be as below:

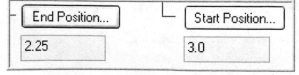

End Position...
2.25

Start Position...
3.0

13. Click on the **Thread cut parameters** tab and makes changes as shown below:

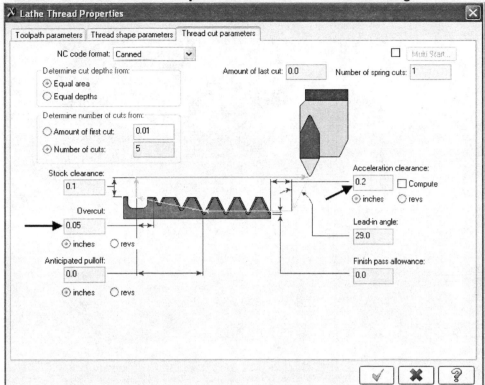

14. Click on the OK icon 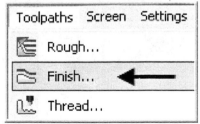.

TASK 13:
FINISH THE RADIUS
➲ In this task you will create a new Tool to machine and finish the 1.5" Radius.

1. From the menu bar select **Toolpaths>Finish...**

2. With the Chaining dialog box set to Partial, click on the radius as shown below:

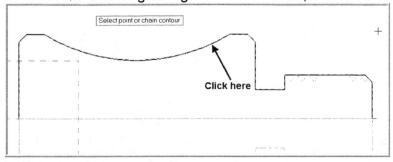

3. Click on the chamfer as shown below left: Arrows should be in the direction as shown below right after clicking on the chamfer.

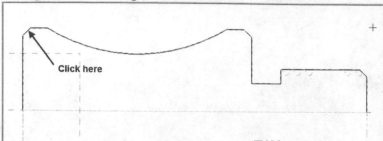

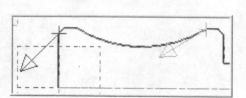

4. Click on OK ✓.
5. Right Click the mouse in the space as indicated by arrow # 1 shown below:
6. Click on **Create new tool...** as indicated by arrow # 2 as shown below:

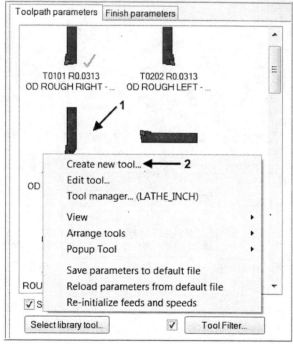

7. Click on the **General Turning** Button as shown below:

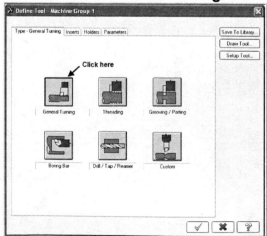

8. Click on the **V (35 deg. Diamond)** insert as shown below:

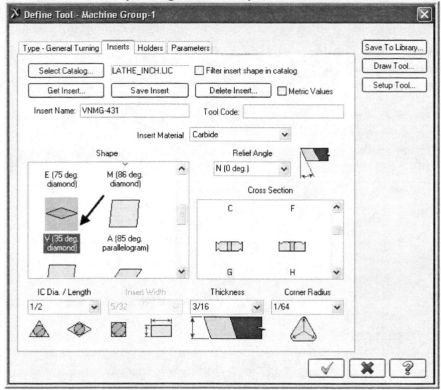

9. Click on the **Holders** Tab.
10. Scroll down and click on the **V (17.5 deg. Side clr.)** as shown below:

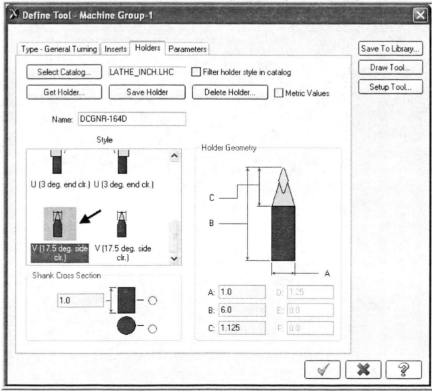

11. Click on the OK icon ✓ .

12. Make any necessary changes as shown below:

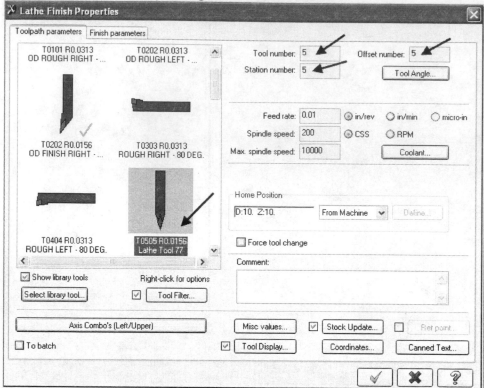

13. Click on the **Finish parameters** tab and make any necessary changes as shown below:

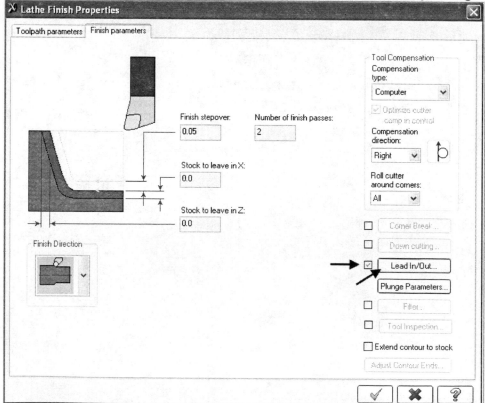

14. Click on the **Lead in/Out Button** as shown above:

15. Make the necessary changes as shown below. In order to adjust the dial (#1), click on the desired location of the arrow:

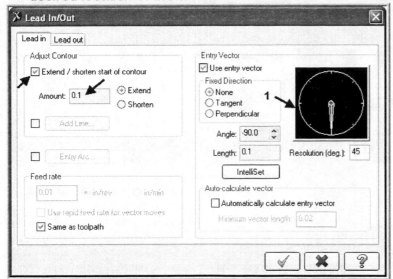

16. Click on the **Lead out Tab** and make the necessary changes as shown below:

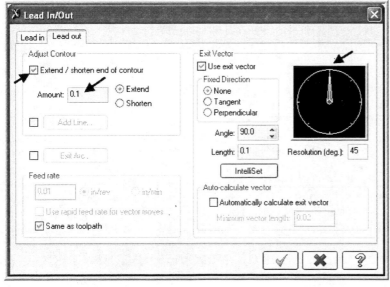

17. Click on OK ✓ to exit the Lead In/out window.

18. Click on the **Plunge Parameters** button as shown below:

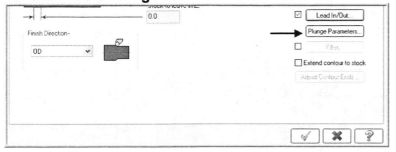

19. Make the necessary changes as shown below:

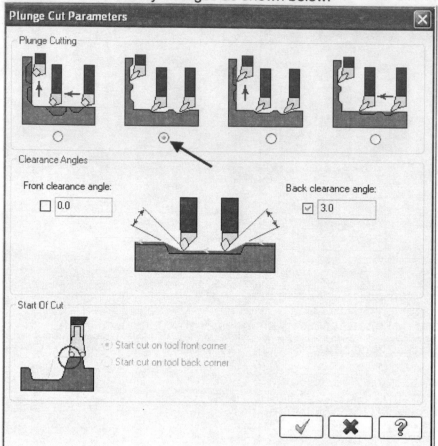

20. Click on Ok [✓] to exit the **Plunge Cut Parameters** window.

21. Click on Ok [✓] to exit the **Lathe Finish parameters** window.

TASK 14:
CUT OFF THE PART

➲ In this task you will cut off the part using **Tool #3 0.125 OD GROOVE RIGHT HAND TOOL**

1. From the menu bar select **Toolpaths>Cutoff...**

2. Pick the end point of the line shown below. Move the cursor over the corner until the visual cue for End point displays and then click on this point.

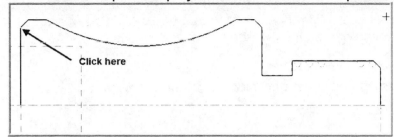

Click here

3. Select **Tool #3 OD GROOVE RIGHT WIDTH .125** tool from the tool list and make any necessary changes as shown below:

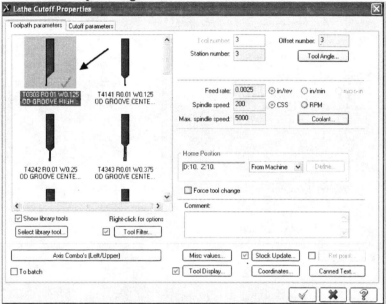

4. Select the **Cutoff parameters** page and make sure the settings are as shown below:

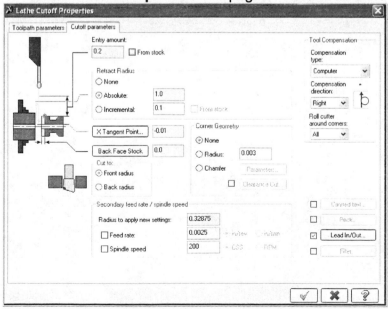

5. Select the OK button [✓] to exit **Lathe Cutoff parameters.**

TASK 15:
VERIFY THE TOOLPATH
➲ Mastercam's Verify utility allows you to use solid models to simulate the machining of a part. The model created by the verification represents the surface finish, and shows collisions, if any exist.

1. In the Toolpaths Manager pick all the operations to backplot by picking the **Select All** icon
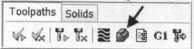

2. Select the **Verify selected operations** icon shown below:

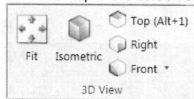

3. **Maximize** the Backplot/Verify window if required.
4. At the top of the screen select the **Isometric** icon and then select **Fit**.

```
┌─────────────────────────────────────┐
│  ⟵⟶          ⬡ Top (Alt+1)          │
│  ⬍    ⬡                              │
│            ⬡ Right                   │
│  Fit  Isometric                      │
│            ⬡ Front ▾                 │
│              3D View                 │
└─────────────────────────────────────┘
```

5. Activate the options shown below in the **Visibility** section of the Home tab. **Initial Stock not** activated.

```
┌──────────────────────────────────────┐
│  ☐ Toolpath    ☑ Stock               │
│  ☑ Tool        ☐ Initial Stock       │
│  ☐ Workpiece   ☑ Fixtures            │
│       Visibility                     │
└──────────────────────────────────────┘
```

6. In the lower right corner of the screen now set the run **Speed** to slow by moving the slider bar pointer over to the left as shown below.

```
┌──────────────────────────────────────┐
│  Speed:   ⬍────────────────          │
│                                      │
└──────────────────────────────────────┘
```

7. Now select the **Play Simulation** button to review the toolpaths.

8. Select the Close button 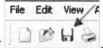 in the top right hand corner to exit Verify.

TASK 16:
SAVE THE UPDATED MASTERCAM FILE

1. Select the save icon from the toolbar

TASK 17:
POST AND CREATE THE CNC CODE FILE

1. Ensure all the operations are selected by picking the **Select All** icon 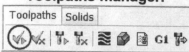 from the **Toolpaths manager.**

2. Select the **Post selected operations** button from the Toolpaths manager.
⊃ **Please Note:** If you cannot see **G1** click on the right pane of the Toolpaths manager window and expand the window to the right.

3. In the Post processing window, make the necessary changes as shown below:

About Post Processing

NC file:
Select this option to save the NC file. The file name and extension are stored in the machine group properties for the selected operation. If you are posting operations from different machine groups or Mastercam files, or batch processing, Mastercam will create several files according to the settings for each machine group.

Edit:
When checked, automatically launches the default text editor with the file displayed so that you can review or modify it.

4. Select the OK button [✓] to continue.

5. Ensure the same name as your Mastercam part file name is displayed in the **NC File name** field.
6. Select the **Save** button.
7. The CNC code file opens up in the default editor.

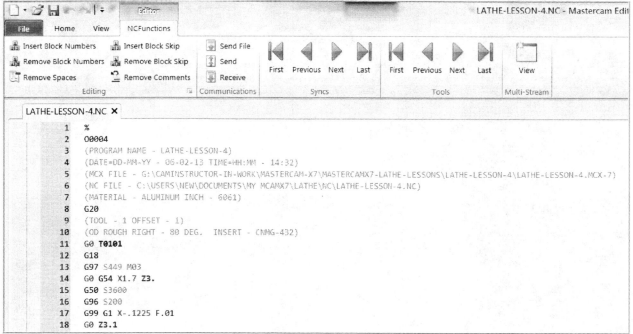

8. Select the ☒ in the top right corner to exit the CNC editor.
9. This completes LATHE-LESSON-4.

LATHE-LESSON-4 EXERCISE

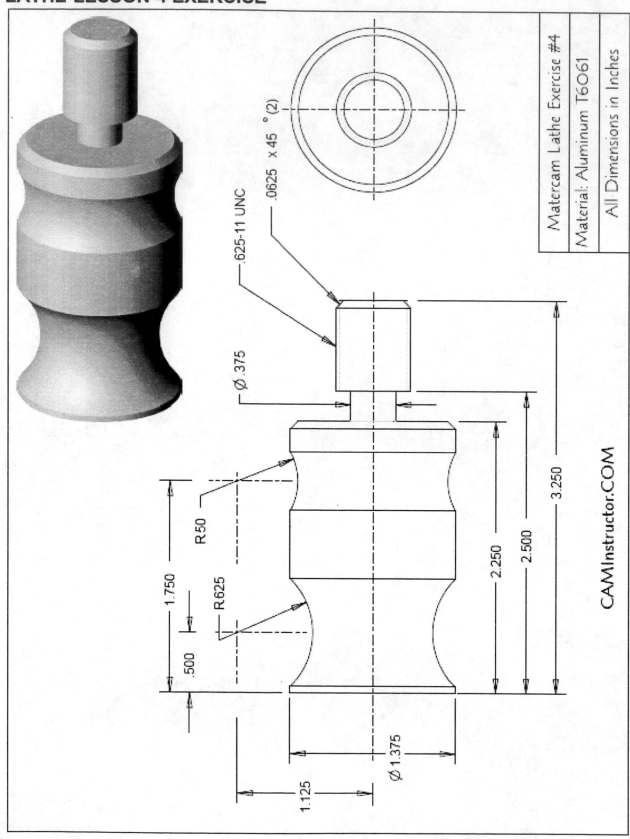

.625-11 UNC

.0625 x 45 ° (2)

Ø .375

R50

R625

1.750

.500

1.125

Ø 1.375

2.250

2.500

3.250

Matercam Lathe Exercise #4

Material: Aluminum T6061

All Dimensions in Inches

CAMInstructor.COM

Mastercam. X⁷
TRAINING
GUIDE

LATHE-LESSON-5
FACE, ROUGH, FINISH, DRILL,
BORE AND CUTOFF

camInstructor

Objectives

You will create the geometry for Lathe Lesson 5, and then generate a toolpath to machine the part on a CNC lathe. This lesson covers the following topics:

➲ **Create a 2-dimensional drawing by:**
Creating lines.
Creating fillets.
Creating chamfers.
Trimming geometry.

➲ **Establish Stock and Chuck Setup settings:**
Stock size.
Chuck Configuration.
Material for the part.
Feed calculation.

➲ **Generate a 2-dimensional lathe toolpath consisting of:**
Lathe Face.
Lathe Rough.
Lathe Finish.
Lathe Drill.
Lathe Cutoff.

➲ **Inspect the toolpath using Mastercam's Verify and Backplot by:**
Launching the Verify function to machine the part on the screen.
Generating the NC- code.

LATHE - LESSON - 5 DRAWING

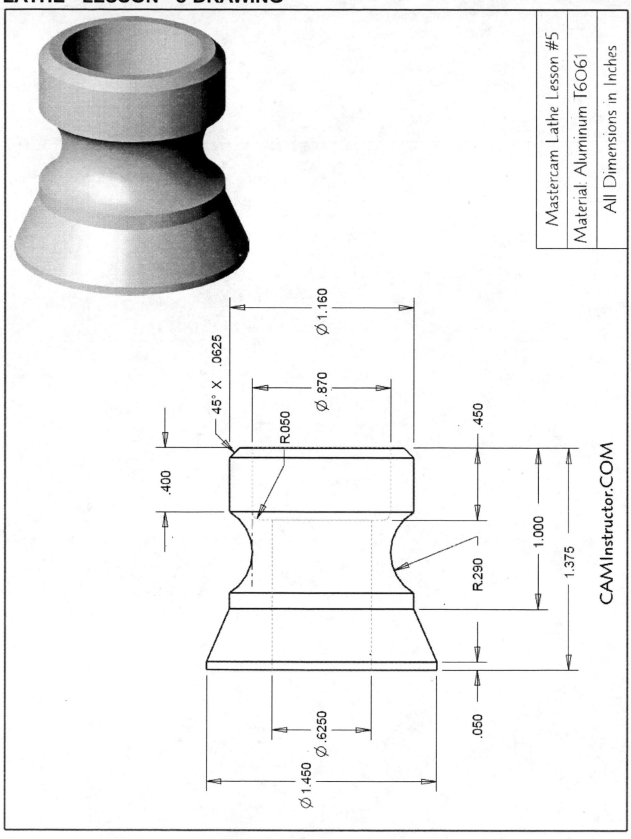

Mastercam Lathe Lesson #5

Material: Aluminum T6061

All Dimensions in Inches

CAMInstructor.COM

TOOL LIST

Seven tools will be used to create this part.
- Tool #1 Face and Rough the outside diameters
- Tool #2 Finish the outside diameters
- Tool #3 Center drill
- Tool #4 0.375 diameter drill
- Tool #5 0.500 diameter drill
- Tool #6 Boring tool
- Tool #7 Cutoff tool

```
            Tool List of LATHE-LESSON-5.MCX-5

Proj./Part No.: 0                Date        : 06/22/10
Drawing No.   : 1                Customer    : -
Prog. No.     : 5                Programmer  : 1
```

```
Tool type      : T0101: specific tool type - OD ROUGH RIGHT - 80 DEG.
Manufact.code  :
Holder/Insert  : DCGNR-164D / CNMG-432
Setup length   :
Spindle RPM    :    200   Feedrate UPR :   0.01   Corner radius :   0.0313
Length offset  :      1   Tool chan. D,Z:  14   ,   8
```

```
Tool type      : T0202: specific tool type - Lathe Tool 75
Manufact.code  :
Holder/Insert  : DCGNR-164D / CNMG-432
Setup length   :
Spindle RPM    :    200   Feedrate UPR :   0.01   Corner radius :   0.0313
Length offset  :      2   Tool chan. D,Z:  14   ,   8
```

```
Tool type      : T0303: specific tool type - CENTER DRILL - .5 DIA.
Manufact.code  :
Holder/Insert  :  /
Setup length   :
Spindle RPM    :   1000   Feedrate UPR :   0.01   Corner radius :   0
Length offset  :      3   Tool chan. D,Z:  10   ,  10
```

```
Tool type      : T0404: specific tool type - DRILL .375 DIA.
Manufact.code  :
Holder/Insert  :  /
Setup length   :
Spindle RPM    :    200   Feedrate UPR :   0.01   Corner radius :   0
Length offset  :      4   Tool chan. D,Z:  14   ,   8
```

```
Tool type      : T0505: specific tool type - DRILL .5 DIA.
Manufact.code  :
Holder/Insert  :  /
Setup length   :
Spindle RPM    :    200   Feedrate UPR :   0.01   Corner radius :   0
Length offset  :      5   Tool chan. D,Z:  14   ,   8
```

```
Tool type      : T0606: specific tool type - ID ROUGH MIN. .375 DIA. - 75 DEG.
Manufact.code  :
Holder/Insert  :  /
Setup length   :
Spindle RPM    :    200   Feedrate UPR :   0.01   Corner radius :   0.0156
Length offset  :      6   Tool chan. D,Z:  14   ,   8
```

```
Tool type      : T0707: specific tool type - OD GROOVE RIGHT - NARROW
Manufact.code  :
Holder/Insert  :  / GC-4125
Setup length   :
Spindle RPM    :    200   Feedrate UPM :    20   Corner radius :   0.01
Length offset  :      7   Tool chan. D,Z:  14   ,   8
```

LESSON - 5 - THE PROCESS

Geometry Creation

TASK 1: Setting the environment
TASK 2: Setting the construction planes
TASK 3: Create the geometry
TASK 4: Create the 0.290" radius
TASK 5: Create the geometry for the bore
TASK 6: Create the chamfers
TASK 7: Save the drawing

Toolpath Creation

TASK 8: Define the stock and chuck parameters
TASK 9: Face the front of the part
TASK 10: Rough the outside diameters
TASK 11: Finish the outside diameters
TASK 12: Center drill hole
TASK 13: Pre drill the 0.625" hole 0.375 diameter
TASK 14: Pre drill the 0.625" hole 0.5 diameter
TASK 15: Rough the bore
TASK 16: Finish the bore
TASK 17: Cut off the part
TASK 18: Verify the toolpath
TASK 19: Save the updated Mastercam file
TASK 20: Post and create the cnc code file

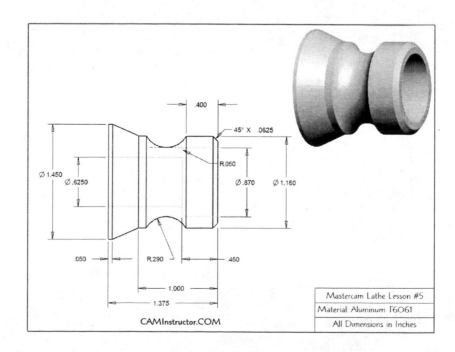

Mastercam Lathe Lesson #5
Material: Aluminum T6061
All Dimensions in Inches

CAMInstructor.COM

Geometry Creation

TASK 1:
SETTING THE ENVIRONMENT

Before starting the geometry creation you should set up the grid and toolbars as outlined in the **Setting the Environment** section at the beginning of this text:
1.   Set up the Grid. This will help identify the location of the origin.
2.   Customize the toolbars to machine a part on the Lathe.
3.   Set the machine type to the default Lathe.

TASK 2:
SETTING THE CONSTRUCTION PLANES:

➲   **Set the Construction Plane to Lathe diameter +D +Z (WCS)**
1.   Click on Planes at the bottom of the screen as shown below:

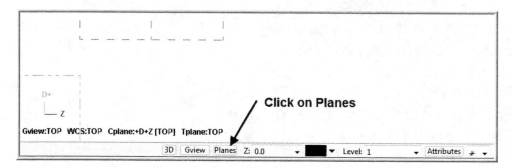

2.   Click on **Lathe diameter>+D +Z (WCS)** as shown below:

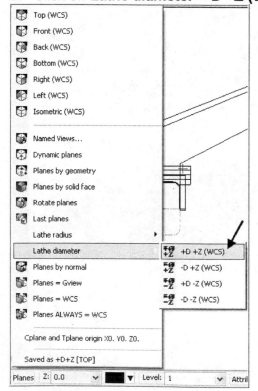

TASK 3:
CREATE THE GEOMETRY
➲ This task explains how to create the geometry of this part. In this lathe part you only need to create **half of the geometry**, the geometry above the center line.
➲ Lines 1 through 6 will be created first and then the radius and chamfer will be created.

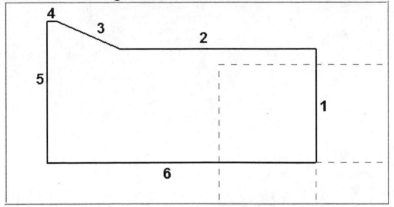

➲ **Create Line #1**
1. Select **Alt-O** on your keyboard to turn off the display of the Toolpaths Manager.
2. Select from the pull down menu **Create>Line>Endpoint...**

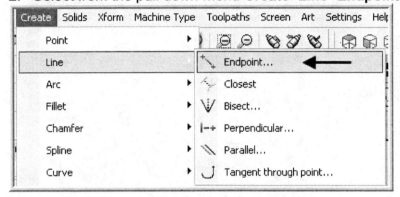

3. The Line ribbon bar appears:

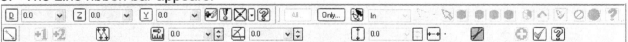

4. Move the cursor over the **center of the grid** and as you get close to the origin a visual cue

appears. This is the cue that will allow you to snap to the **origin**. With this visual cue highlighted pick the **origin.**

AutoCursor: Visual Cues detects and highlights endpoints and midpoints of curves, lines, arc center points, and point entities. In addition, AutoCursor can snap to angle, nearest, tangent, perpendicular, horizontal, and vertical conditions.

⮑ The following are Mastercam Visual Cues:

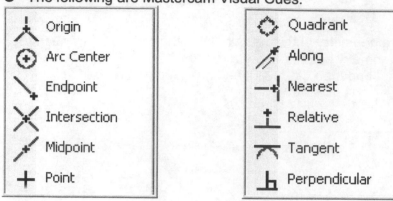

⟊ Origin	◇ Quadrant
⊕ Arc Center	⟋ Along
⟍ Endpoint	⊣⊢ Nearest
⤬ Intersection	⊥ Relative
⟋ Midpoint	⌒ Tangent
✛ Point	⌐ Perpendicular

5. You are next prompted to **"Specify the second endpoint"**. On the left hand side of the Line ribbon bar click on the **Multi-Line** button to activate it as shown below by the arrow:

6. Click in the **D** value space (Diameter) (as shown by the arrow below) and enter a value of **1.16**. Hit the Enter key and enter a value of **0 for the Z**, hit the Enter key again and enter a value of **0 for the Y** and hit Enter.

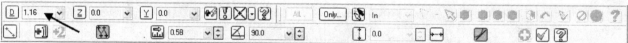

7. A vertical line should be visible as shown below:

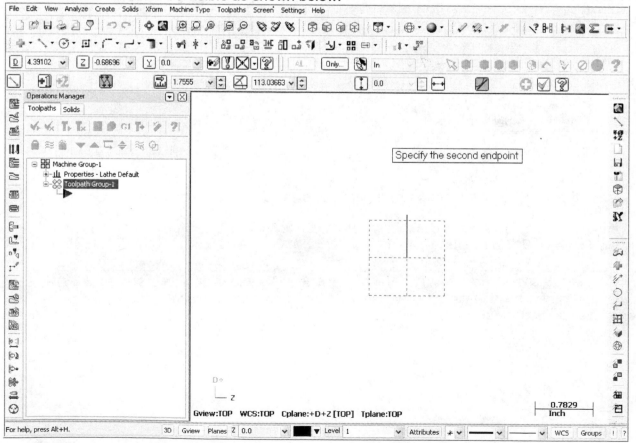

⊃ **Create Line #2**

8. **"Specify the second endpoint"**; Type in **1.16 in D** hit Enter, type in **-1.0 in Z** and hit Enter and type in **0.0 in Y** and hit Enter.

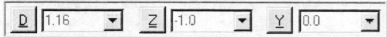

⊃ **Create Line #3**

9. **"Specify the second endpoint"**; Type in **1.45 in D** hit Enter, type in **-1.375-0.05 in Z** and hit Enter and type in **0.0 in Y** and hit Enter.

⊃ **Create Line #4**

10. **"Specify the second endpoint"**; Type in **1.45 in D** hit Enter, type in **-1.375 in Z** and hit Enter and type in **0.0 in Y** and hit Enter.

⊃ **Create Line #5**

11. **"Specify the second endpoint"**; Type in **0.0 in D** hit Enter, type in **-1.375 in Z** and hit Enter and type in **0.0 in Y** and hit Enter.

⊃ **Create Line #6**

12. **"Specify the second endpoint"**; Move the cursor over the **center of the grid** and as you get close to the origin a visual cue appears. 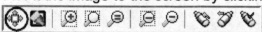 Click on this point.

13. Click on the **OK** icon  to complete this feature.

14. Fit the image to the screen by clicking on the **Fit** icon as shown below:

15. Then unzoom by clicking on the **Un-zoom Previous / .5** icon as shown below:

16. Your geometry should look like the figure below.

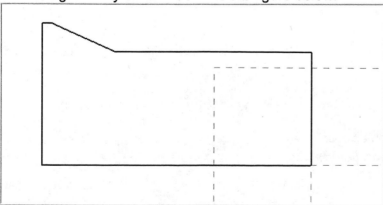

TASK 4:
CREATE THE 0.290" RADIUS
➲ In this task you will create the 0.290 arc. It is an arc tangent to a line and passes through a point.

➲ **Create the line the arc is tangent to.**
1. Select from the pull down menu: **Create>Line>Parallel....**
2. On the graphics screen you are prompted: Select a line and the Line Parallel ribbon bar appears.
3. To satisfy the prompt **Select a line**, select the line shown below.

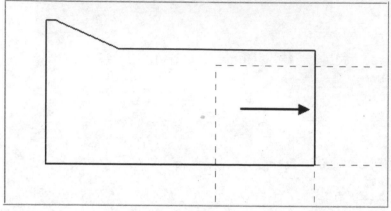

4. To satisfy the next prompt **Select the point to place a parallel line through** move the cursor to the left of the line and pick a point.
5. For the **Distance** input **0.4** then hit **enter**.

6. On the ribbon bar click on **Apply** ⊕ to fix the entity,
7. To satisfy the prompt **Select a line**, select the line shown below.

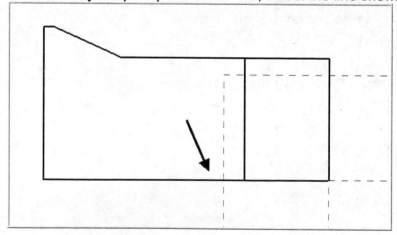

8. To satisfy the next prompt **Select the point to place a parallel line through** move the cursor above the line and pick a point.
9. For the **Distance** input **0.870/2** then hit **enter**
10. Click on the OK icon ☑ to complete this feature.

11. The completed geometry is shown below:

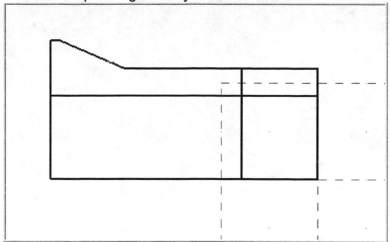

➲ **Create the 0.290" Arc**

12. Select **Create>Arc> Arc Tangent...**

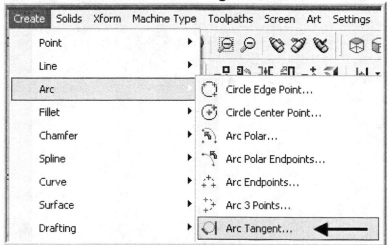

13. The **Arc Tangent** ribbon bar appears and you are prompted to **Select the entity that the arc is to be tangent to**.

14. Click on the **Tangent point** icon to activate it as shown above. Ensure the icon is pressed down to signal that it is activated.

15. Click in the space for **Radius** (shown above) and enter a value of **0.290** and then hit the **enter** key.

16. To satisfy the prompt **Select the entity that the arc is to be tangent to** move the cursor over the line shown below and select it:

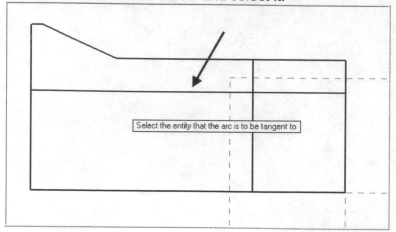

17. To satisfy the prompt **Specify the thru point** move the cursor over the endpoint of the line shown below. When the visual cue for endpoint appears click on this point.

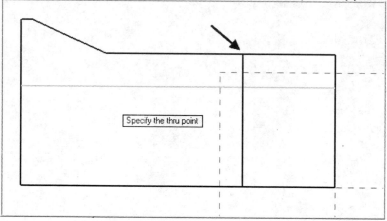

18. After selecting this endpoint you a confronted with a selection of arcs. The prompt changes to **Select an arc**. Select the arc in the position shown below:

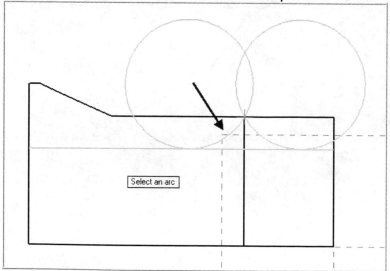

19. Click on the OK icon [✓] to complete this feature.

20. The completed arc is shown below.

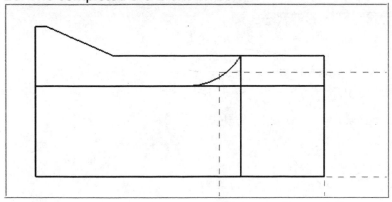

◒ **Trim the Arc**
21. Select **Edit>Trim/Break>Trim/Break/Extend**
22. The Trim / Extend / Break ribbon bar appears and you are prompted to **Select the entity to trim/extend**.
23. Click on the **Trim 1 entity** button as shown below:

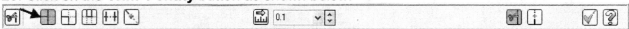

24. Now at the prompt **Select the entity to trim/extend** select the arc at **position 1,**
25. The prompt changes to **Select the entity to trim/extend to**, select the line at **position 2**

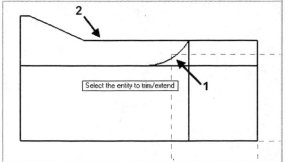 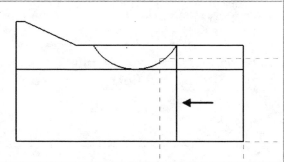

26. Click on the OK icon [✓] to complete this feature.
27. The geometry should look like the image above right.
28. **Delete** the construction line shown above right. Select the line and hit the Delete key on your keyboard.

TASK 5:
CREATE THE GEOMETRY FOR THE BORE
➲ In this task you will create the geometry that make up the bore of this part

1. Select from the pull down menu: **Create>Line>Parallel....**
2. **On the graphics screen you are prompted**: **Select a line** and the Line Parallel ribbon bar appears.
3. To satisfy the prompt **Select a line**, select the line shown below.

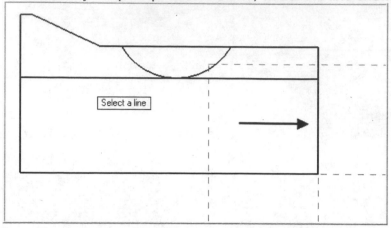

4. To satisfy the next prompt **Select the point to place a parallel line through** move the cursor to the left of the line and pick a point.
5. For the **Distance** input **0.450** then hit **enter**.

6. On the ribbon bar click on **Apply** ⊕ to fix the entity.
7. To satisfy the prompt **Select a line**, select the line shown below.

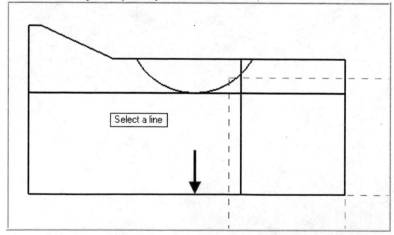

8. To satisfy the next prompt **Select the point to place a parallel line through** move the cursor above the line and pick a point.
9. For the **Distance** input **0.625/2** then hit **enter**.
10. Click on the OK icon ✓ to complete this feature.

⊃ Create 0.050 fillet

11. Select **Create>Fillet>Entities...**

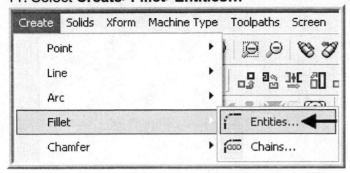

12. On the Fillet ribbon bar enter **0.05 for the radius**. Ensure the **Style** of radius is set to **Normal** and the trim button is depressed to turn the **trim on**.

13. When prompted to **Fillet: Select an entity,** select Line 1 and 2 as shown below. The fillet radius appears at the corner of line 1 and 2.

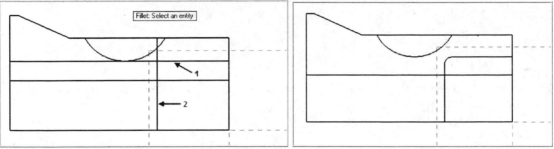

14. Click on the OK icon [✓] to complete this feature.

⊃ Trim the bore

15. Select **Edit>Trim/Break>Trim/Break/Extend.**

16. The Trim / Extend / Break ribbon bar appears and you are prompted to **Select the entity to trim/extend**.

17. Click on the **Trim 2 entity** button as shown below:

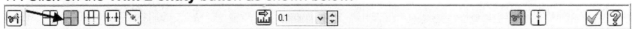

18. Now at the prompt **Select the entity to trim/extend** select the line at **position 1,**

19. The prompt changes to **Select the entity to trim/extend to**, select the line at **position 2**

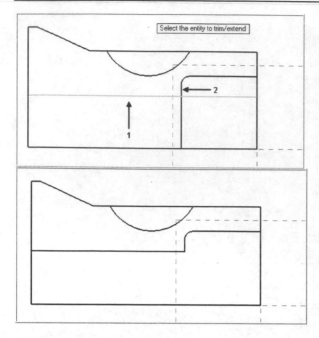

20. The trimmed geometry should look like the image above right.

⊃ **Trim the .290 arc**

21. Now click on the Divide icon ⊞.
22. The prompt changes to **Select the curve to divide.** Move the cursor over the line and select it as shown below left.

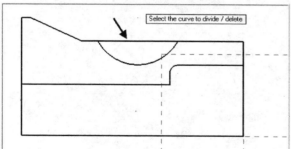 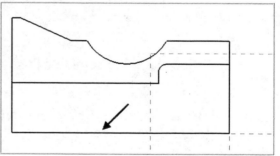

23. Click on the OK icon ☑ to complete this feature. The line is trimmed back to the two closest intersections as shown above right:
24. **Delete** the construction line shown above right. Select the line and hit the delete key on your keyboard.

TASK 6:
CREATE THE CHAMFER

➲ **Create Chamfer 45 degrees x .0625.**

1. Select **Create>Chamfer>Entities...**

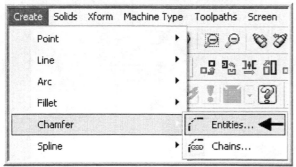

2. You are prompted to ⎹Select line or arc⎸.
3. Click in the Distance window as shown below and type in **.0625** and hit enter:

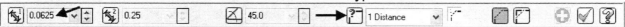

4. Ensure the 1 Distance option is selected as shown above.
5. Click on line 1 and then line 2 as shown below:

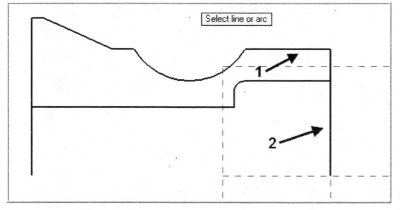

6. Click on the OK icon ⎹✓⎸ to complete this feature.
7. The completed geometry should look like the image below:

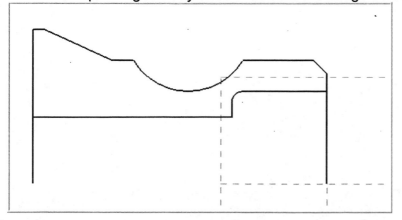

TASK 7:
SAVE THE DRAWING

1. Select **File.**
2. Select **Save as.**
3. In the **"File name"** box, type **"Lathe-Lesson-5".**
4. Save to an appropriate location.
5. Select the Save button to save the file and complete this function.

File name:	LATHE-LESSON-5	▾
Save as type:	Mastercam X7 Files (*.MCX-7)	▾

Toolpath Creation

TASK 8:
DEFINING THE STOCK AND CHUCK PARAMETERS

1. Fit the image to the screen by clicking on the Fit icon .
2. Then unzoom by clicking on the **Un-zoom Previous / .5** icon as shown below:

3. Ensure your screen looks like the image below:
   a. The Toolpaths Manager is open, if it is not Select Alt and O on your keyboard to open it.
   b. The properties icon displays Lathe Default. If it is not refer to **Setting the Environment** chapter at the beginning of the book.
   c. The Lathe Lesson-5 Geometry is displayed.

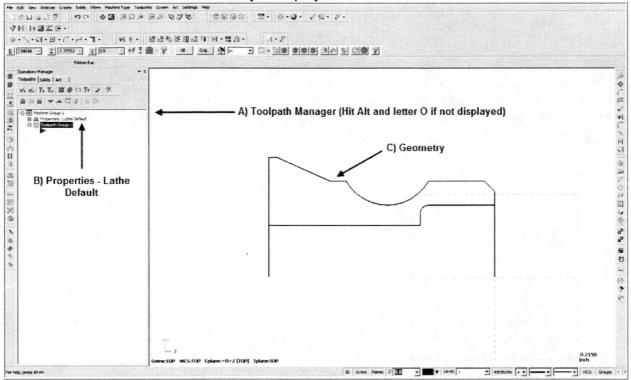

4. Select the plus in front of **Properties** to expand the Machine Group Properties.

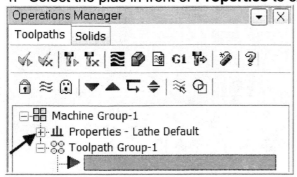

5. Select **Stock setup** in the Toolpaths Manager window.

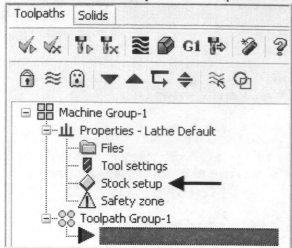

6. Select the **Stock Properties** button in the **Stock Setup** page as shown in the screenshot below:

➲ Note: To learn how to complete this section of the **Stock Setup** refer to the **Tips and Techniques** section on the **Mastercam Training Guide – Lathe DVD** that accompanies this book.

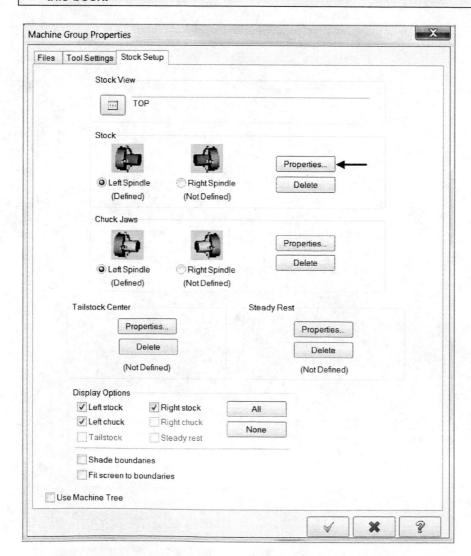

7. In the **Machine Component Manager-Stock** window click on the **Geometry** button and select **Cylinder** as shown below:

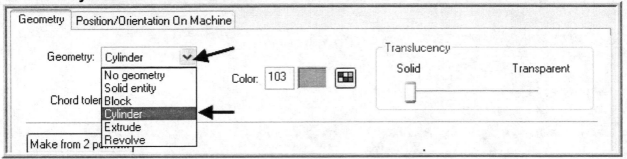

8. In the **Stock** setup set the values as shown below:

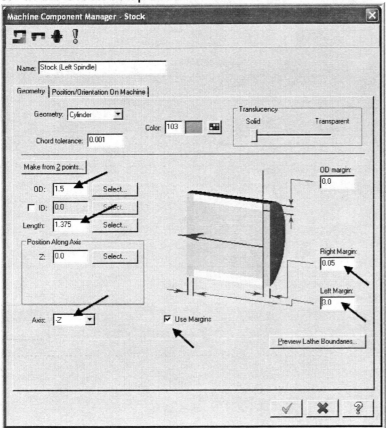

9. Click on the OK icon ☑ to complete this feature.

10. Select the **Chuck Properties** button in the **Stock Setup** page as shown in the screenshot below:

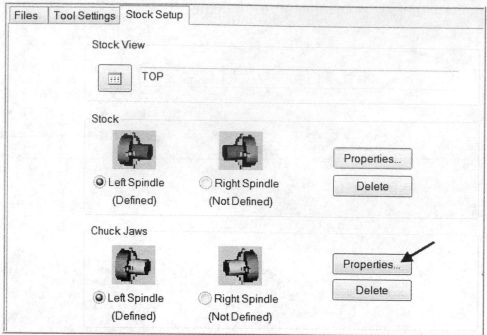

11. In the **Chuck Jaws** setup set the values as shown below:

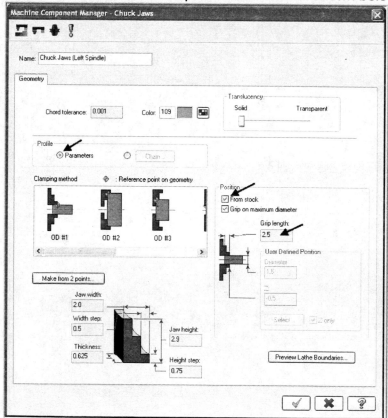

12. Click on the OK icon ☑ to complete this feature.

13. Click on the **Tool Settings** page and make changes as shown below:

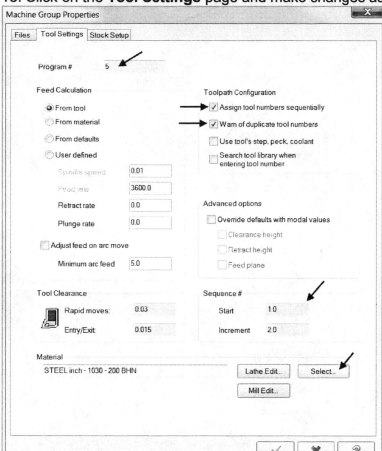

14. To change the **Material** type to Aluminium 6061 pick the **Select** button at the bottom of the Tool Settings page.

15. At the **Material List** dialog box open the Source drop down list and select **Lathe – library.**

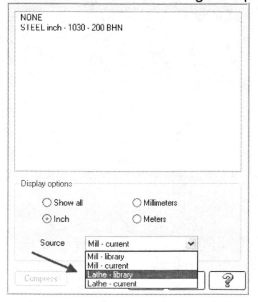

16. From the **Default Materials** list select **ALUMINIUM inch - 6061** and then select ☑.

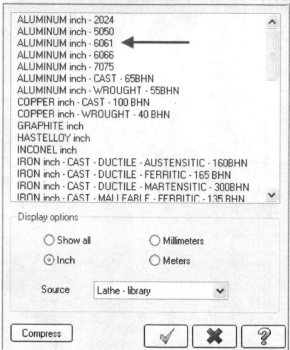

17. Select the OK button ☑ again to complete this Stock Setup function.
18. Zoom out by clicking on the **Un-Zoom Previous / .5** icon

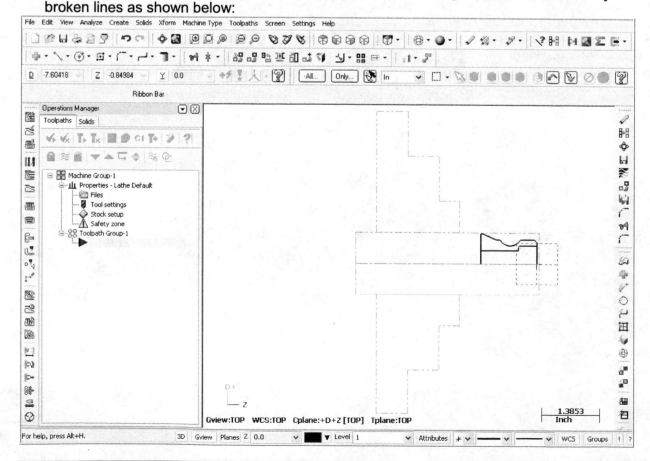 to view the stock setup outline as indicated by broken lines as shown below:

TASK 9:
FACE THE FRONT OF THE PART:
➲ In this task you will use a facing tool to face the front of the part in one cut.

1. Select the **Screen Fit** icon to fit the part to the screen ⬦.

2. Then select the **Un-Zoom previous / .5** icon. 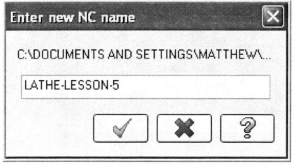 This function reduces the size of the displayed geometry to 50% of its current size.

3. From the menu bar select **Toolpaths>Face...**

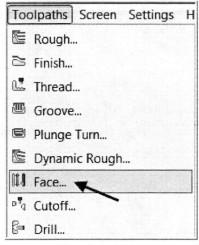

| Toolpaths | Screen | Settings | H |

🄴 Rough...

🄳 Finish...

🄻 Thread...

🄶 Groove...

🄾 Plunge Turn...

🄴 Dynamic Rough...

🄸🄸 Face...

🄲 Cutoff...

🄳 Drill...

4. When prompted to **"Enter new NC name"** Ensure **LATHE-LESSON-5** is entered as shown below and then select the OK button ✓.

Enter new NC name ✕

C:\DOCUMENTS AND SETTINGS\MATTHEW\...

LATHE-LESSON-5

✓   ✗   ?

➲ After selecting the OK button you are confronted with Toolpath parameters page. The first task here will be to select Tool #1 a Roughing – 80 deg.

5. Click on **Tool 0101 Roughing – 80 degree** and ensure the settings are the same as in the Toolpath parameters page as shown below:

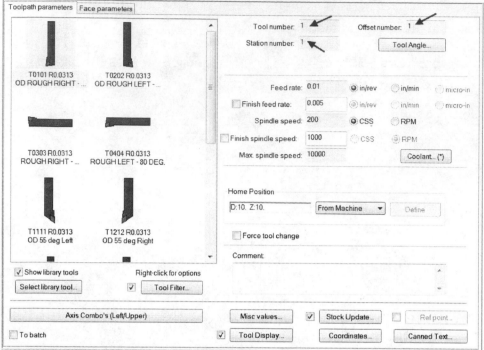

6. Select the **Face parameters** page and make changes as shown below:

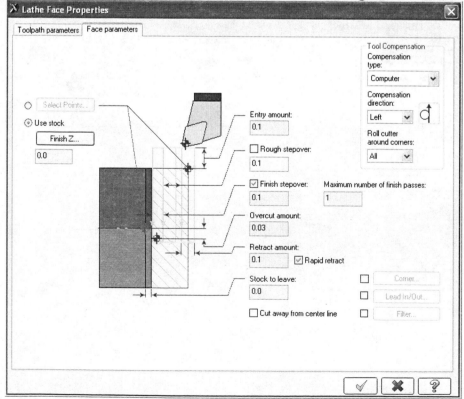

7. Select the OK button [✓] to complete this **Lathe Face** operation.

TASK 10:
ROUGH THE OUTSIDE DIAMETERS
- ○ In this task you will use a Lathe toolpath called Lathe Quick Toolpaths.
- ○ You will use the same tool as used for the previous facing operation **Tool #1 an OD Rough-Right – 80 deg.**

1. From the menu bar select **Toolpaths>Quick>Rough...**

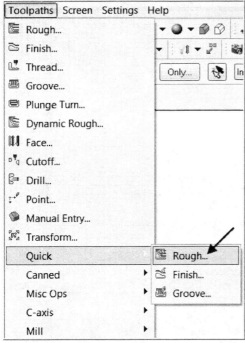

2. In the **Chaining** window Chaining mode is set to **Partial** by default.

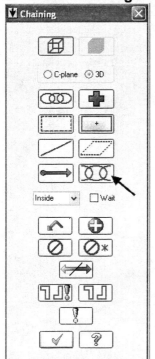

3. Select the chamfer, Line 1 as the start of the **Partial chain**.

After you have selected the chamfer **ensure** that the arrow is pointing towards the part as shown below. If it is not select the reverse button in the Chaining dialog box

---

4. Then select Line 2 as the end entity in this chain.

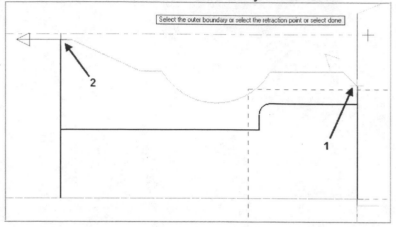

5. Select the OK button [✓] to exit the Chaining dialog window.
6. In the **Quick Tool parameters** page select the **Tool #1 an Roughing – 80 deg** and make any necessary changes as shown below:

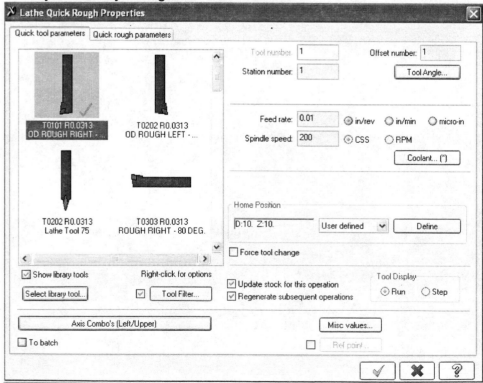

7. Select the **Quick Rough parameters** page and make any necessary changes as shown below:

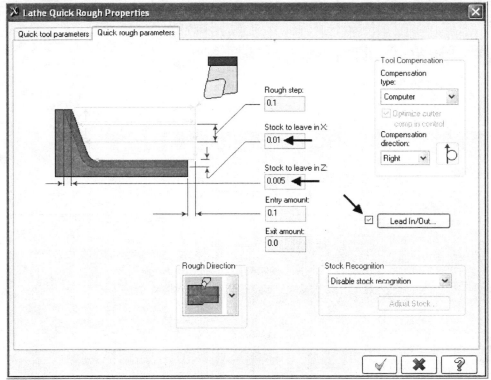

8. Select the **Lead In/Out** button, then select the **Lead out** page and extend the contour by .2 as shown below:

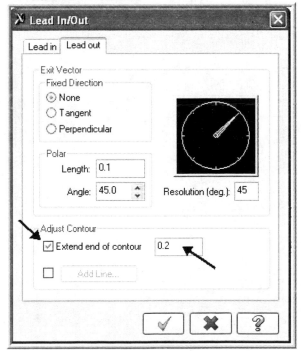

9. Select the OK button 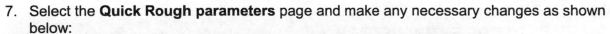 to exit this function.
10. Select the OK button to exit Rough Parameters.

TASK 11:
FINISH THE OUTSIDE DIAMETERS
➲ In this task you will create a new tool to finish the outside diameters.

1. From the menu bar select **Toolpaths>Finish...**

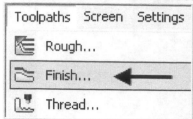

2. Click on the **Last** button [⌃] in the chaining dialog box to select the previous chain.
3. Select the OK button [✓] to exit the Chaining dialog window.
4. Right Click the mouse in the space as indicated by arrow # 1 shown below:
5. Click on **Create new tool...** as indicated by arrow # 2 as shown below:

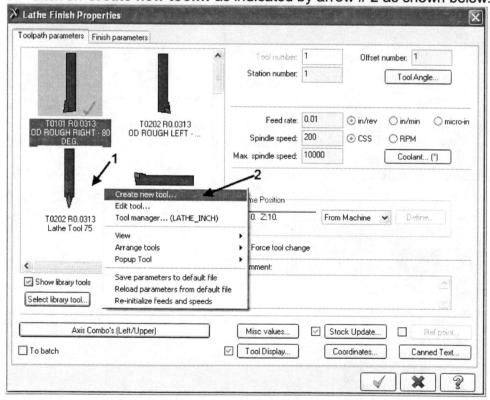

6. Click on the **General Turning** Button as shown below:

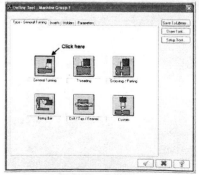

7. Scroll down and click on the **V (35 deg. Diamond)** insert as shown below:

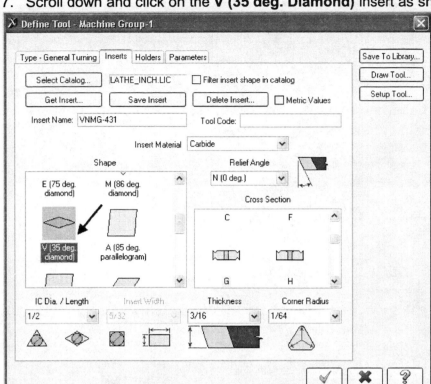

8. Click on the **Holders** Tab.
9. Scroll down and click on the **V (17.5 deg. Side clr.)** as shown below:

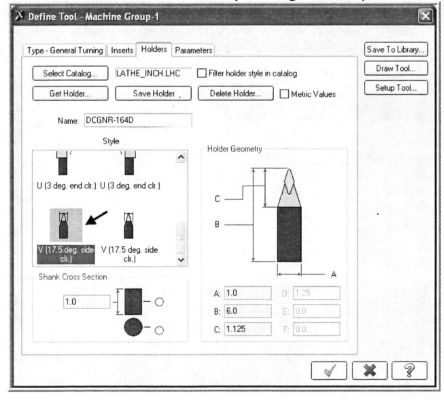

10. Click on the **Parameters** page and at the bottom of this page set the compensation for this tool as shown below:

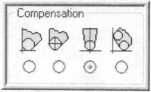

11. Click on the OK icon [✓].

12. Make any necessary changes as shown below:

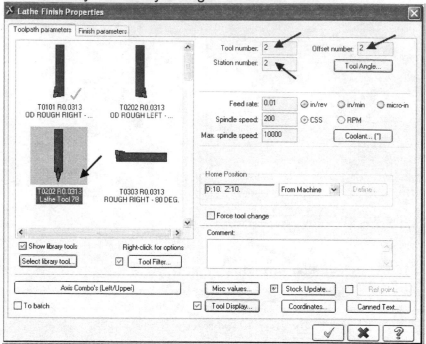

13. Click on the **Finish parameters** tab and make any necessary changes as shown below:

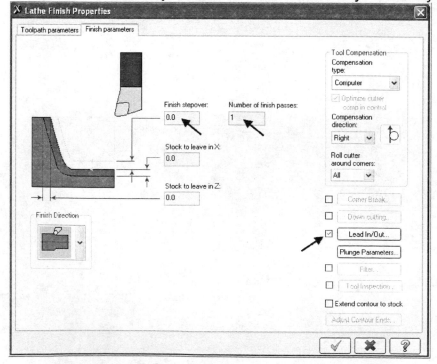

14. Click on the **Lead in/Out** button as shown above:

15. Make the necessary changes as shown below. In order to adjust the entry vector dial, click on the desired location of the arrow on the dial:

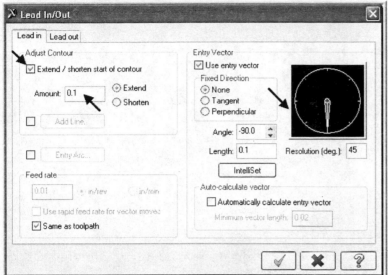

16. Click on the **Lead out** tab and make the necessary changes as shown below:

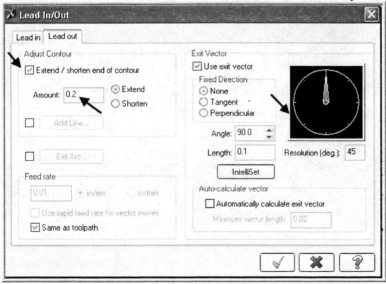

17. Click on OK ![check] to exit the Lead In/out window.

18. Click on the Plunge Parameters button [Plunge Parameters...].

19. Make the necessary changes as shown below:

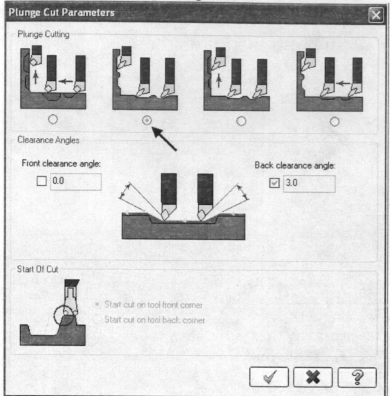

20. Click on **OK** [✓] to exit the **Plunge Cut parameters** window.

21. Click on **OK** [✓] to exit the **Lathe Finish parameters** window.

TASK 12:
CENTER DRILL HOLE
➲ In this task you will center drill .2" depth using **Tool #3 Centre Drill - .25 diameter.**

1. From the menu bar select **Toolpaths>Drill…**

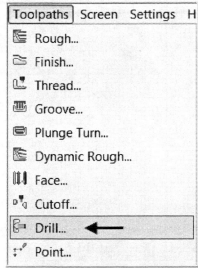

2. Select the **Centre Drill .25 diameter** tool from the tool list and make changes as shown below:

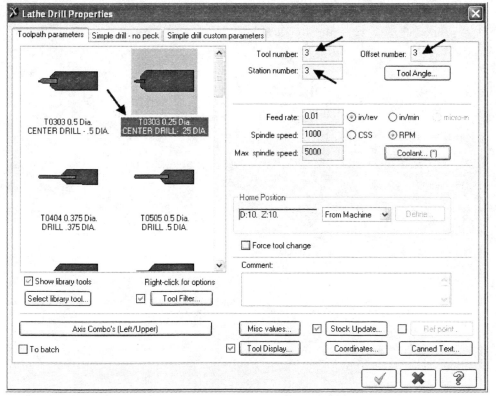

3. Select the Simple drill – no peck page and make changes as shown below:

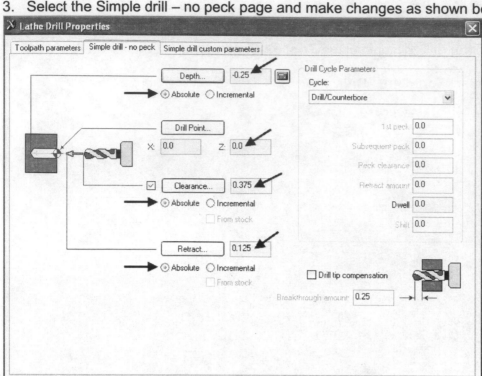

4. Select the OK button ✓ to exit Simple drill – no peck.

TASK 13:
PRE DRILL THE 0.625" HOLE 0.375 DIAMETER

➲ In this task you will pre drill the .625" hole through the part using **Tool #4 Drill - .375 diameter.**

1. From the menu bar select **Toolpaths>Drill...**

2. Scroll down and select the **Drill - .375 diameter** tool from the tool list and make changes as shown below:

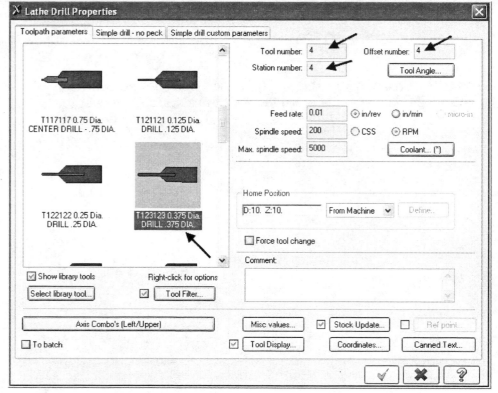

3. Select the **Simple drill – no peck** page and make changes as shown below. This hole will be **peck drilled through the part**. Make changes as shown below:

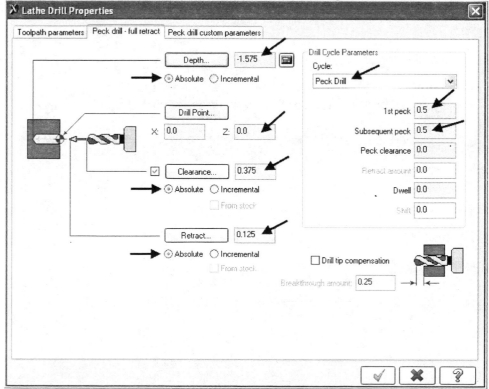

4. Select the OK button to exit Peck drill – full retract.

TASK 14:
PRE DRILL THE 0.625" HOLE 0.5 DIAMETER

‣ In this task you will peck drill through the part with a 0.5 diameter drill prior to boring.
‣ You will copy the previous peck drill operation and then modify into this peck drilling operation.

1. On the left of the screen in the Toolpaths Manager the 0.375 drill peck drilling operation is the **fifth** operation. To copy this operation hold down the **Right mouse button** over the folder for this operation. Keep holding the right mouse button down and drag below the red arrow and release.
2. Select **Copy after** from this menu.

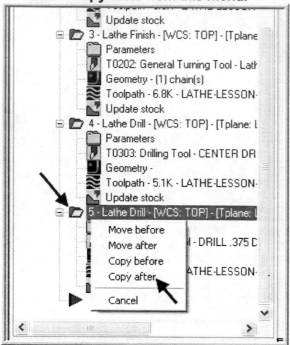

3. Move the Insert arrow 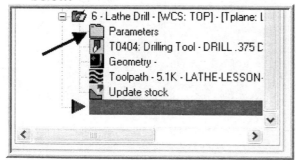 to the bottom of the list of operations by clicking the ▼ icon on the Toolpaths Manager toolbar.
4. In the Toolpaths Manager click on the folder Parameters for the **sixth** operation as shown below:

5. Select the **Toolpath parameters** page.
6. Scroll down and select the .50 diameter drill, as shown below
7. Make changes to the Toolpath parameters page as shown below.

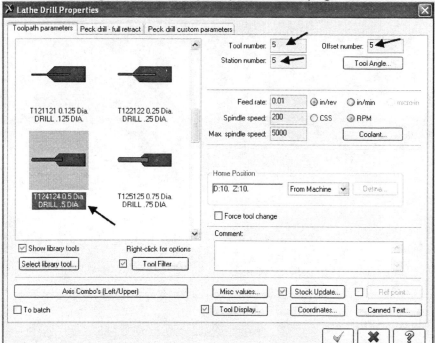

8. Select the **Peck drill – full retract** page and make changes as shown below.

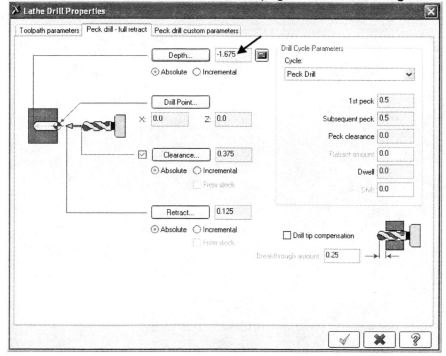

9. Select the OK button [✓] to exit Peck drill – full retract.

10. Select the Regenerate all dirty operations button [🔧×] to remove the red X from the drilling operation you have just edited. You need to update the toolpath with the new parameters you have just input.

TASK 15:
ROUGH THE BORE
➲ In this task you will use a boring tool to rough out the 0.870 and 0.625 diameter bores.

1. From the menu bar select **Toolpaths>Rough...**

2. In the **Chaining** window Chaining mode is set to **Partial** by default.
3. Select Line 1 as the start of the **Partial chain**.

After you have selected the first line **ensure** that the arrow is pointing towards the part as shown below. If it is not select the reverse button in the Chaining dialog box

4. Then select Line 2 as the end entity in this chain.

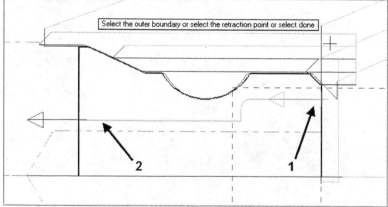

5. Select the OK button ☑ to exit the Chaining dialog window.

6. In the **Toolpath parameters** page scroll down and select a boring tool **ID ROUGH MIN .375 DIA – 75 deg** and make any necessary changes as shown below:

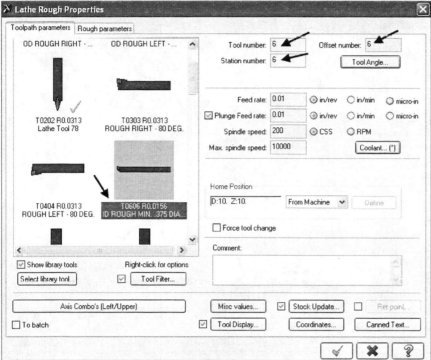

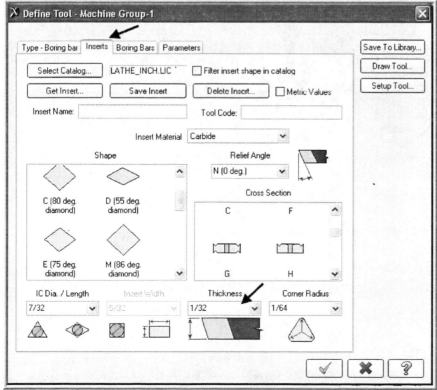

7. Double click on the picture ![] for this boring tool in the tool list window.
8. On the **Inserts** page change the thickness of this insert to 1/32 as shown below:

9. Select the OK button ☑ to exit this function.

10. Select the Rough **parameters** page and make any necessary changes as shown below:

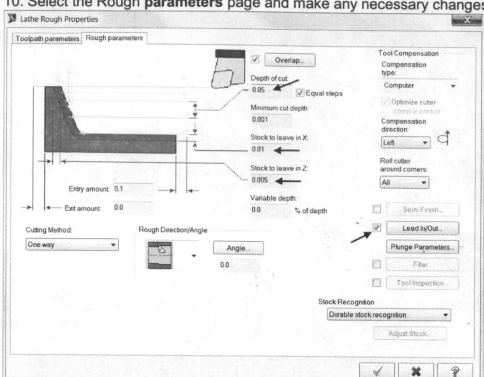

11. Select the **Lead In/Out** button select the Lead out page and extend the contour by .1 as shown below:

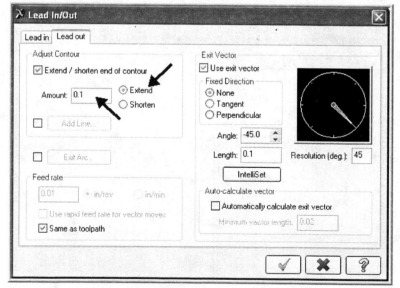

12. Select the OK button to exit this function.
13. Select the OK button to exit **Rough** Parameters.

TASK 16:
FINISH THE BORE

⊃ In this task you will use the same boring tool as used for the previous rouging operation.

1. From the menu bar select **Toolpaths>Quick>Finish...**

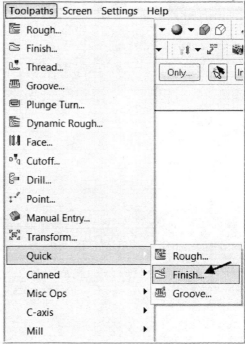

2. In the **Quick Toolpath parameters** page select **Tool #6 a boring tool ID ROUGH MIN .375 DIA – 75 deg** and make any necessary changes as shown below:

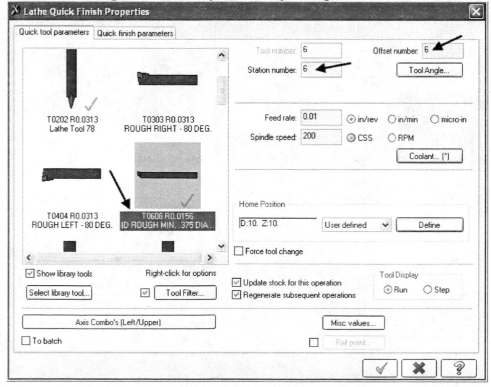

3. Select the **Quick finish parameters** page and make any necessary changes as shown below. Open up the drop down menu for operation and select the operation at the bottom of the list, this is the previous rough boring operation.

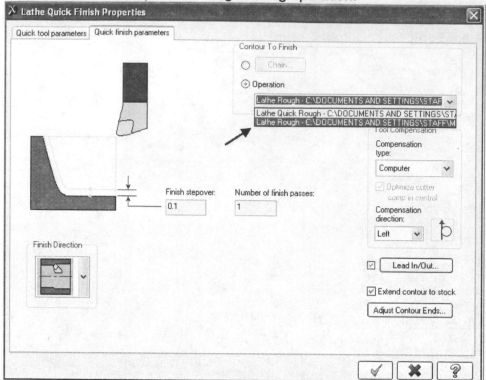

4. Select the **Lead In/Out button** select the Lead out page and extend the contour by .1 as shown below:

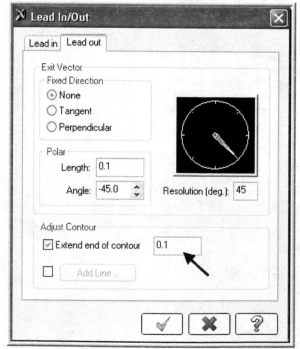

5. Select the OK button ☑ to exit this function.
6. Select the OK button ☑ to exit **Quick finish** parameters.

TASK 17:
CUT OFF THE PART
➲ In this task you will cut off the part using **Tool #7 0.125 OD GROOVE RIGHT HAND TOOL**

1. From the menu bar select **Toolpaths>Cutoff...**

2. Select **Alt-T** on the keyboard to hide the display of toolpaths.
3. When prompted to **Select cutoff boundary point** pick the end point of the line shown below. Move the cursor over the corner until the visual cue for End point displays and then click on this point.

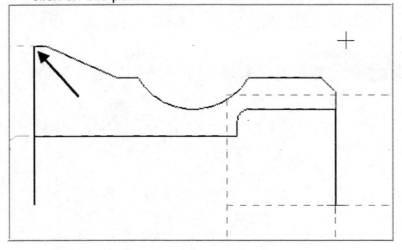

4. Select **OD GROOVE RIGHT WIDTH .125** tool from the tool list and make any necessary changes as shown below:

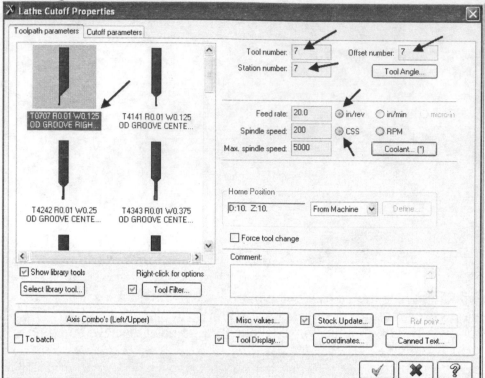

5. Select the **Cutoff parameters** page and make sure the settings are as shown below:

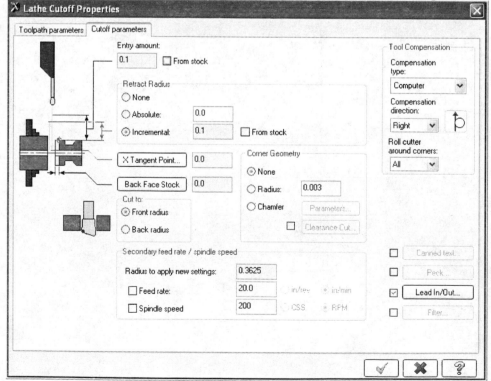

6. Select the OK button ☑ to exit **Lathe Cutoff parameters.**

TASK 18:
VERIFY THE TOOLPATH

➲ Mastercam's Verify utility allows you to use solid models to simulate the machining of a part. The model created by the verification represents the surface finish, and shows collisions, if any exist.

1. In the Toolpaths Manager pick all the operations to backplot by picking the **Select All** icon
     .

2. Select the **Verify selected operations** icon shown below:

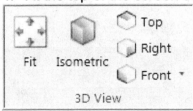

3. **Maximize** the Backplot/Verify window if required.
4. At the top of the screen select the **Isometric** icon and then select **Fit**.

> Fit   Isometric   ◎ Top
>   ◎ Right
>   ◎ Front ▾
>   3D View

5. Activate the options shown below in the **Visibility** section of the Home tab. **Initial Stock not activated.**

> ☐ Toolpath   ☑ Stock
> ☑ Tool   ☐ Initial Stock
> ☐ Workpiece   ☑ Fixtures
>   Visibility

6. In the lower right corner of the screen now set the run **Speed** to slow by moving the slider bar pointer over to the far left as shown below.

> Speed: ⬇

7. Now select the **Play Simulation** button to review the toolpaths.

8. Select the Close button 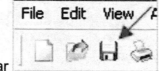 in the top right hand corner to exit Verify.

TASK 19:
SAVE THE UPDATED MASTERCAM FILE

1. Select the save icon from the toolbar

TASK 20:
POST AND CREATE THE CNC CODE FILE

1. Ensure all the operations are selected **by picking the** Select All **icon**  **from the** Toolpaths manager.

2. Select the **Post selected operations** button from the Toolpaths manager.
 ➲ **Please Note:** If you cannot see **G1** click on the right pane of the Toolpaths manager window and expand the window to the right.

3. In the Post processing window, make the necessary changes as shown below:

About Post Processing

NC file:
Select this option to save the NC file. The file name and extension are stored in the machine group properties for the selected operation. If you are posting operations from different machine groups or Mastercam files, or batch processing, Mastercam will create several files according to the settings for each machine group.

Edit:
When checked, automatically launches the default text editor with the file displayed so that you can review or modify it.

4. Select the OK button ✓ to continue.

5. Ensure the same name as your Mastercam part file name is displayed in the **NC File name** field.
6. Select the **Save** button.
7. The CNC code file opens up in the default editor.

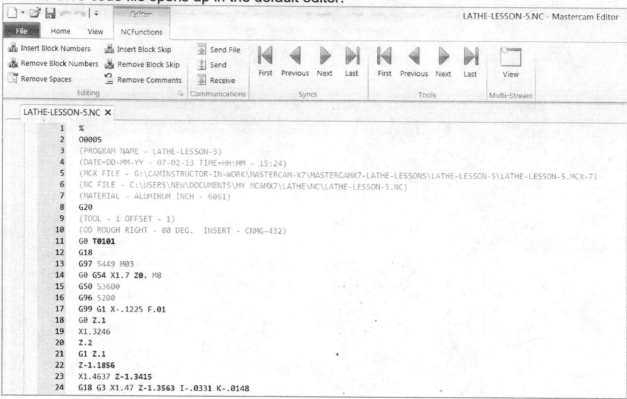

8. Select the ☒ in the top right corner to exit the CNC editor.
9. This completes LATHE-LESSON-5.

LATHE-LESSON-5 EXERCISE

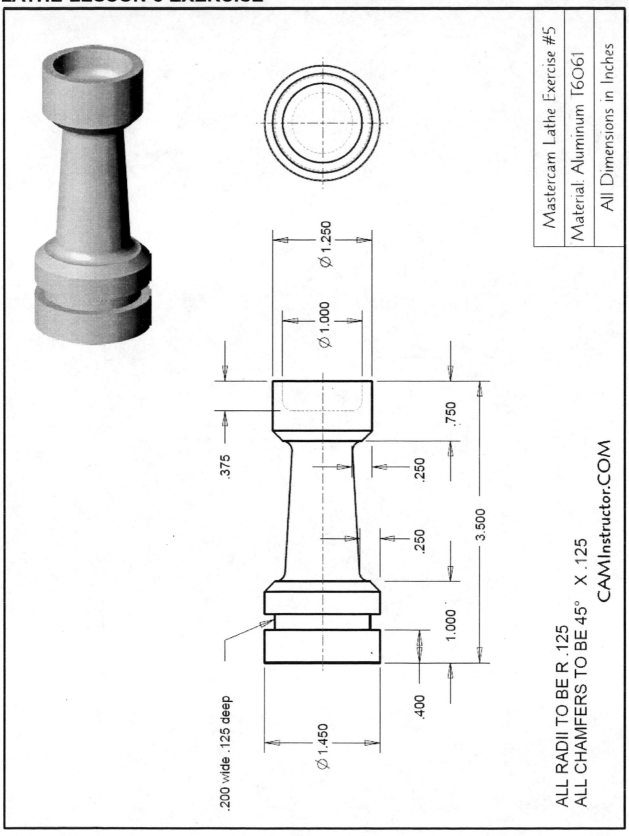

Ø 1.250

Ø 1.000

.375

.750

.250

.250

3.500

1.000

.400

Ø 1.450

.200 wide .125 deep

ALL RADII TO BE R .125
ALL CHAMFERS TO BE 45° X .125

CAMInstructor.COM

Mastercam X⁷

TRAINING GUIDE

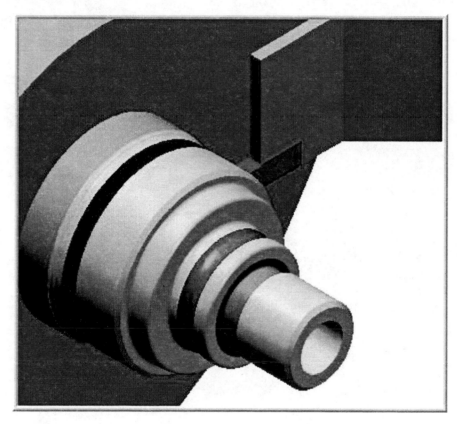

LATHE-LESSON-6
FACE, QUICK ROUGH AND FINISH,
DRILL, GROOVE AND CUTOFF

camInstructor

Objectives

You will create the geometry for Lathe Lesson 6, and then generate a toolpath to machine the part on a CNC lathe. This lesson covers the following topics:

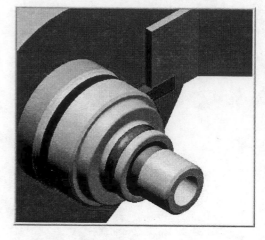

➲ **Create a 2-dimensional drawing by:**
Creating lines.
Creating fillets.
Creating chamfers.
Trimming geometry.

➲ **Establish Stock and Chuck Setup settings:**
Stock size.
Chuck Configuration.
Material for the part.
Feed calculation.

➲ **Generate a 2-dimensional lathe toolpath consisting of:**
Lathe Face.
Lathe Quick Rough.
Lathe Quick Finish.
Lathe Finish.
Lathe Drill.
Lathe Groove.
Lathe Cutoff.

➲ **Inspect the toolpath using Mastercam's Verify and Backplot by:**
Launching the Verify function to machine the part on the screen.
Generating the NC- code.

LATHE - LESSON-6 DRAWING

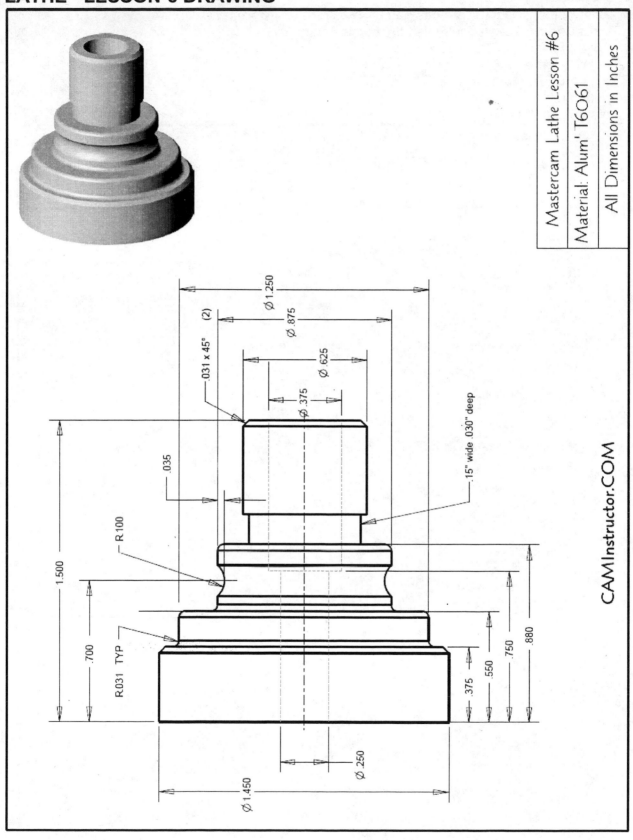

Mastercam Lathe Lesson #6

Material: Alum' T6061

All Dimensions in Inches

Ø 1.250

Ø .875

.031 x 45° (2)

Ø 625

Ø 375

.035

.15" wide .030" deep

R 100

1.500

.700

R031 TYP

.880

.750

.550

.375

Ø .250

Ø 1.450

CAMInstructor.COM

TOOL LIST
Six tools will be used to create this part.
- Tool #1 Face, Rough and Finish the outside diameters
- Tool #2 Finish the 0.1 radius
- Tool #3 Center drill
- Tool #4 0.250 diameter drill
- Tool #5 0.375 End Mill
- Tool #6 Cutoff tool

```
              Tool List of LATHE-LESSON-6.MCX-5

 Proj./Part No.: 0               Date      : 06/23/10
 Drawing No.   : 1               Customer  : -
 Prog. No.     : 6               Programmer: 1

   Tool type    : T0101: specific tool type - OD ROUGH RIGHT - 80 DEG.
   Manufact.code:
   Holder/Insert: DCGNR-164D / CNMG-432
   Setup length :
   Spindle RPM  :    200    Feedrate UPR :    0.01   Corner radius :   0.0313
   Length offset:      1    Tool chan. D,Z:   14  ,    8

   Tool type    : T0202: specific tool type - Lathe Tool 75
   Manufact.code:
   Holder/Insert: DCGNR-164D / CNMG-432
   Setup length :
   Spindle RPM  :    200    Feedrate UPR :    0.01   Corner radius :   0.0938
   Length offset:      2    Tool chan. D,Z:   14  ,    8

   Tool type    : T0303: specific tool type - CENTER DRILL- .25 DIA.
   Manufact.code:
   Holder/Insert: /
   Setup length :
   Spindle RPM  :   1000    Feedrate UPR :    0.01   Corner radius :      0
   Length offset:      3    Tool chan. D,Z:   10  ,   10

   Tool type    : T0404: specific tool type - DRILL .25 DIA.
   Manufact.code:
   Holder/Insert: /
   Setup length :
   Spindle RPM  :    200    Feedrate UPR :    0.01   Corner radius :      0
   Length offset:      4    Tool chan. D,Z:   14  ,    8

   Tool type    : T0505: specific tool type - END MILL .375 DIA. - .007R
   Manufact.code:
   Holder/Insert: /
   Setup length :
   Spindle RPM  :    200    Feedrate UPR :    0.01   Corner radius :   0.007
   Length offset:      5    Tool chan. D,Z:   14  ,    8

   Tool type    : T0606: specific tool type - OD GROOVE RIGHT - NARROW
   Manufact.code:
   Holder/Insert: / GC-4125
   Setup length :
   Spindle RPM  :    200    Feedrate UPM :     20    Corner radius :   0.01
   Length offset:      6    Tool chan. D,Z:   14  ,    8
```

LESSON - 6 - THE PROCESS

Geometry Creation

TASK 1:	Setting the environment
TASK 2:	Setting the construction planes
TASK 3:	Create the geometry
TASK 4:	Create the 0.100" radius
TASK 5:	Create the chamfers
TASK 6:	Create the fillet radii
TASK 7:	Create the geometry for the bore
TASK 8:	Save the drawing

Toolpath Creation

TASK 9:	Define the stock and chuck parameters
TASK 10:	Face the front of the part
TASK 11:	Rough the outside diameters
TASK 12:	Finish the outside diameters
TASK 13:	Finish the 0.1 radius
TASK 14:	Center drill hole
TASK 15:	Peck Drill the 0.250" Hole
TASK 16:	Drill the 0.375" Hole
TASK 17:	Cut the Groove
TASK 18:	Cut off the part
TASK 19:	Verify the toolpath
TASK 20:	Save the updated Mastercam file
TASK 21:	Post and create the cnc code file

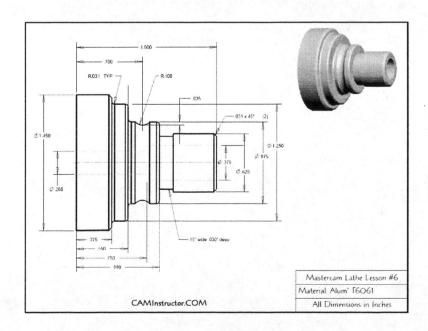

Mastercam Lathe Lesson #6
Material: Alum' T6061
All Dimensions in Inches

CAMInstructor.COM

Geometry Creation

TASK 1:
SETTING THE ENVIRONMENT

Before starting the geometry creation you should set up the grid and toolbars as outlined in the **Setting the Environment** section at the beginning of this text:
1. Set up the Grid. This will help identify the location of the origin.
2. Customize the toolbars to machine a part on the Lathe.
3. Set the machine type to the default Lathe.

TASK 2:
SETTING THE CONSTRUCTION PLANES:

⇒ **Set the Construction Plane to Lathe diameter +D +Z (WCS)**
1. Click on Planes at the bottom of the screen as shown below:

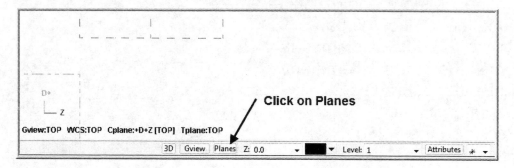

2. Click on Lathe diameter>+D +Z (WCS) as shown below:

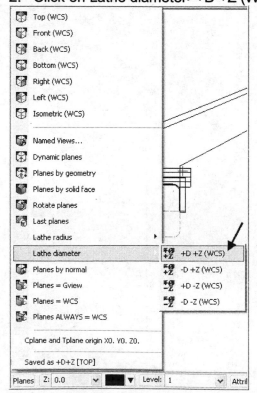

TASK 3:
CREATE THE GEOMETRY

1. This task explains how to create the geometry of this part. In this lathe part you only need to create **half of the geometry**, the geometry above the center line.
2. Lines 1 through 12 will be created first and then the radius and chamfer will be created.

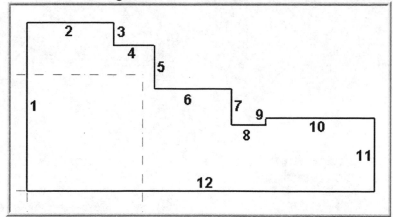

⮑ **Create Line #1**
1. Select **Alt-O** on your keyboard to turn off the display of the Toolpaths Manager.
2. Select from the pull down menu **Create>Line>Endpoint...**

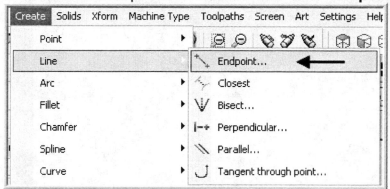

3. The Line ribbon bar appears:

4. Move the cursor over the **center of the grid** and as you get close to the origin a visual cue appears. This is the cue that will allow you to snap to the **origin**. With this visual cue highlighted pick the **origin.**

AutoCursor: Visual Cues detects and highlights endpoints and midpoints of curves, lines, arc center points, and point entities. In addition, AutoCursor can snap to angle, nearest, tangent, perpendicular, horizontal, and vertical conditions.

⊃ The following are Mastercam Visual Cues:

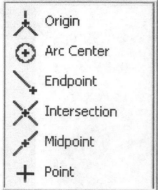

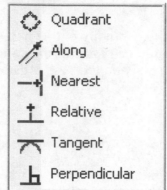

5. You are next prompted to **"Specify the second endpoint"**. On the left hand side of the Line ribbon bar click on the **Multi-Line** button to activate it as shown below by the arrow:

6. Click in the **D** value space (Diameter) and enter a value of **1.45**. Hit the Enter key and enter a value of **0 for the Z**, hit the Enter key again and enter a value of **0 for the Y** and hit Enter.

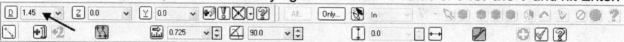

7. A vertical line should be visible as shown below:

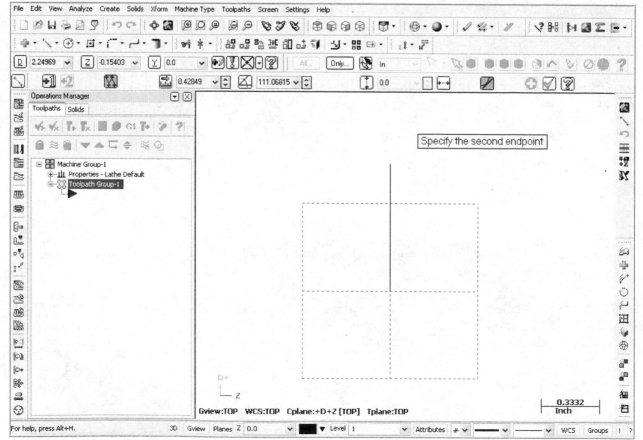

➭ **Create Line #2**

8. **"Specify the second endpoint"**; Type in **1.45 in D** hit Enter, type in **0.375 in Z** and hit Enter and type in **0.0 in Y** and hit Enter.

➭ **Create Line #3**

9. **"Specify the second endpoint"**; Type in **1.250 in D** hit Enter, type in **0.375 in Z** and hit Enter and type in **0.0 in Y** and hit Enter.

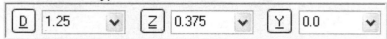

➭ **Create Line #4**

10. **"Specify the second endpoint"**; Type in **1.250 in D** hit Enter, type in **0.550 in Z** and hit Enter and type in **0.0 in Y** and hit Enter.

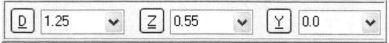

➭ **Create Line #5**

11. **"Specify the second endpoint"**; Type in **0.875 in D** hit Enter, type in **0.550 in Z** and hit Enter and type in **0.0 in Y** and hit Enter.

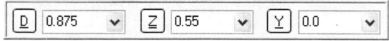

➭ **Create Line #6**

12. **"Specify the second endpoint"**; Type in **0.875 in D** hit Enter, type in **0.880 in Z** and hit Enter and type in **0.0 in Y** and hit Enter.

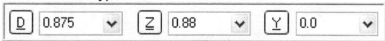

➭ **Create Line #7**

13. **"Specify the second endpoint"**; Type in **0.625-0.06 in D** hit Enter, type in **0.880 in Z** and hit Enter and type in **0.0 in Y** and hit Enter.

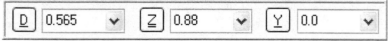

➭ **Create Line #8**

14. **"Specify the second endpoint"**; Type in **0.625-0.06 in D** hit Enter, type in **0.880+0.15 in Z** and hit Enter and type in **0.0 in Y** and hit Enter.

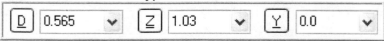

➭ **Create Line #9**

15. **"Specify the second endpoint"**; Type in **0.625 in D** hit Enter, type in **0.880+0.15 in Z** and hit Enter and type in **0.0 in Y** and hit Enter.

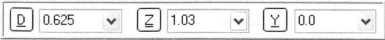

➲ **Create Line #10**

16. **"Specify the second endpoint"**; Type in **0.625 in D** hit Enter, type in **1.500 in Z** and hit Enter and type in **0.0 in Y** and hit Enter.

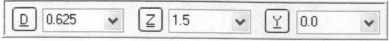

➲ **Create Line #11**

17. **"Specify the second endpoint"**; Type in **0 in D** hit Enter, type in **1.500 in Z** and hit Enter and type in **0.0 in Y** and hit Enter.

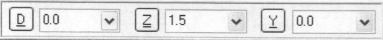

➲ **Create Line #12**

18. **"Specify the second endpoint"**; Move the cursor over the **center of the grid** and as you get close to the origin a visual cue appears.  Click on this point.

19. Click on the **OK** icon  to complete this feature.

20. Fit the image to the screen by clicking on the **Fit** icon as shown below:

21. Then unzoom by clicking on the **Un-Zoom Previous / .5** icon as shown below:

22. Your geometry should look like the figure below:

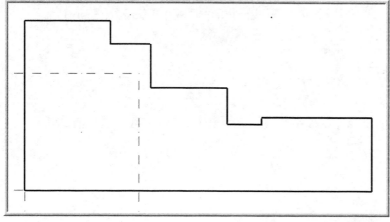

TASK 4:
CREATE THE 0.100" RADIUS

➲ In this task you will create the 0.100 arc. The center position and radius are known.

1. Select **Create>Arc>Arc Polar...**

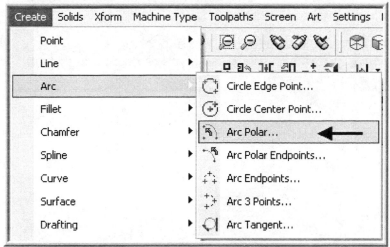

2. The **Arc Polar** ribbon bar appears and you are prompted to **Enter the center point**. Click on the **FastPoint** icon as shown below and enter the coordinates for the center of the arc **0.875-0.07+0.2 , 0.7** and then hit enter.

3. The prompt now changes to **Sketch the initial angle**. Click in the space for **radius** and enter **0.1** and then hit the **tab key twice** to move over to the start angle.
4. Input a **Start angle of 180** and hit the tab key.
5. For the **End angle** input **0** and then hit enter.

6. Click on the OK icon [✓] to complete this feature.
7. The completed arc is shown below:

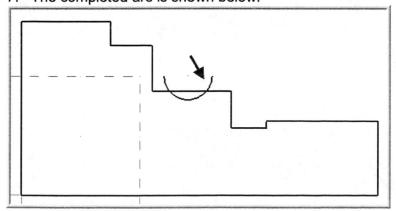

⊃ **Trim the Arc**

8. Select **Edit>Trim/Break>Trim/Break/Extend**
9. The Trim / Extend / Break ribbon bar appears and you are prompted to **Select the entity to trim/extend**.
10. Click on the **Trim 1 entity** button as shown below:

11. Now at the prompt **Select the entity to trim/extend** select the arc at position 1,
12. The prompt changes to **Select the entity to trim/extend** to, select the remaining entities in the order shown below.

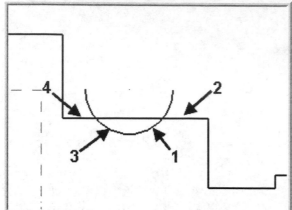
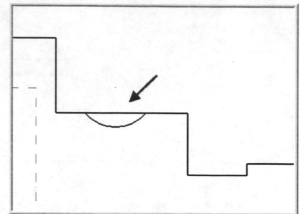

13. The entities are trimmed as shown above right.

14. Now click on the **Divide** icon [+··+].
15. The prompt changes to **Select the curve to divide.** Move the cursor over the line and select it as shown below left.

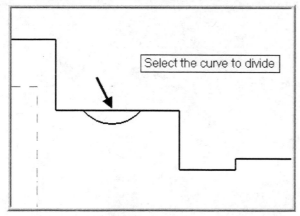
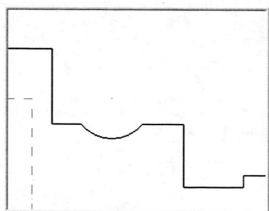

16. Click on the OK icon [✓] to complete this feature.
17. The line is trimmed back to the two closest intersections as shown above right:

TASK 5:
CREATE THE CHAMFERS

➲ **Create the two chamfers 45 degrees x .031.**

1. Select **Create>Chamfer>Entities...**

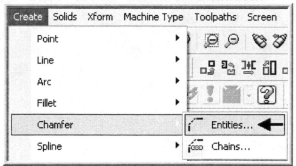

2. You are prompted to | Select line or arc |.
3. Click in the **Distance** window as shown below and type in **0.031** and hit enter:

4. Ensure the **1 Distance** option is selected and **Trim is on** as shown above:
5. Click on line 1 and then line 2 as shown below. Next on line 3 and line 4.

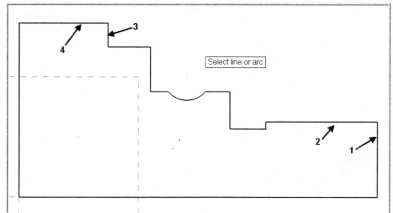

6. Click on the OK icon [✓] to complete this feature.
7. The completed geometry should look like the image below:

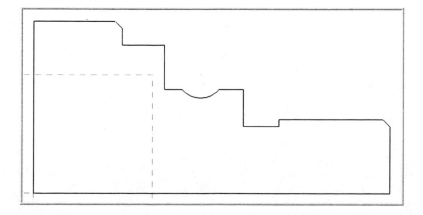

TASK 6:
CREATE THE FILLET RADII

➲ In this task you will create the 0.031 fillet radii in four places.

1. Select **Create>Fillet>Entities...**

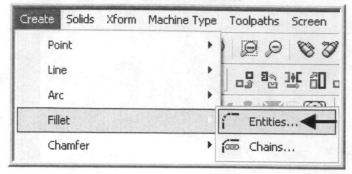

2. On the Fillet ribbon bar enter **0.031 for the radius** and hit enter. Ensure the **Style** of radius is set to **Normal** and the trim button is depressed to turn the **trim on**.

3. When prompted to **Fillet: Select an entity,** select Line 1 and 2 and the select the remaining entities in the order shown below:

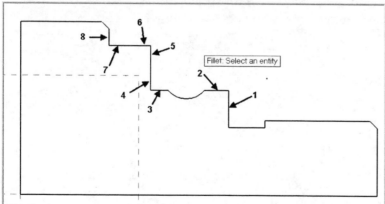

4. Click on the OK icon ☑ to complete this feature. The completed geometry is shown below:

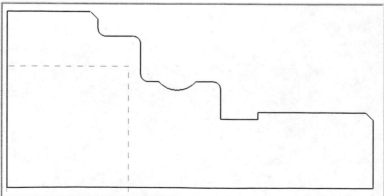

TASK 7:
CREATE THE GEOMETRY FOR THE BORE
➲ In this task you will create the geometry that make up the bore of this part

1. Select from the pull down menu: **Create>Line>Parallel....**
2. **On the graphics screen you are prompted**: **Select a line** and the Line Parallel ribbon bar appears.
3. To satisfy the prompt **Select a line**, select the line shown below.

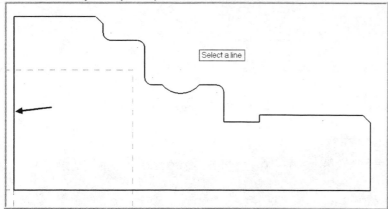

4. To satisfy the next prompt **Select the point to place a parallel line through** move the cursor to the right of the line and pick a point.
5. For the **Distance** input **0.750** then hit **enter**.

6. On the ribbon bar click on **Apply** to fix the entity,
7. To satisfy the prompt **Select a line**, select the line shown below.

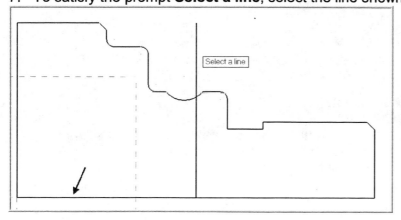

8. To satisfy the next prompt **Select the point to place a parallel line through** move the cursor above the line and pick a point.
9. For the **Distance** input **0.250/2** then hit **enter**

10. On the ribbon bar click on **Apply** to fix the entity.

11. To satisfy the prompt **Select a line**, select the line shown below:

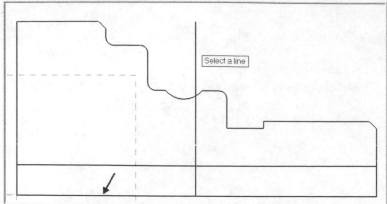

12. To satisfy the next prompt **Select the point to place a parallel line through** move the cursor above the line and pick a point.

13. For the **Distance** input **0.375/2** then hit **enter**

14. Click on the OK icon 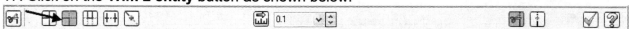 to complete this feature. The completed geometry is shown below:

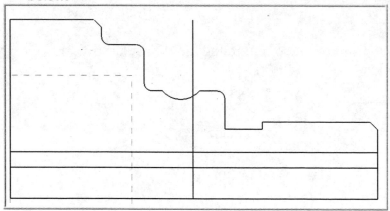

➲ **Trim the bore**

15. Select **Edit>Trim/Break>Trim/Break/Extend**

16. The Trim / Extend / Break ribbon bar appears and you are prompted to **Select the entity to trim/extend**.

17. Click on the **Trim 2 entity** button as shown below:

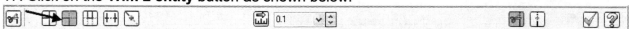

18. Now at the prompt **Select the entity to trim/extend** select the line at **position 1,**
19. The prompt changes to **Select the entity to trim/extend to**, select the line at **position 2**
20. Now at the prompt **Select the entity to trim/extend** select the line at **position 3,**
21. The prompt changes to **Select the entity to trim/extend to**, select the line at **position 4**

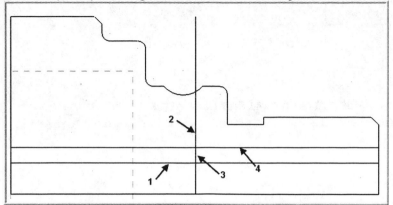

22. Click on the OK icon [✓] to complete this feature.

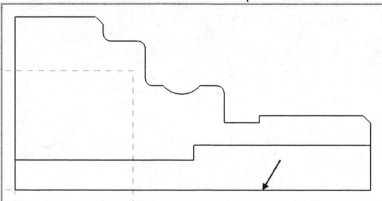

23. **Delete** the construction line shown above. Select the line and hit the delete key on your keyboard.

TASK 8:
SAVE THE DRAWING

1. Select **File.**
2. Select **Save as.**
3. In the **"File name"** box, type **"Lathe-Lesson-6".**
4. Save to an appropriate location.
5. Select the Save button to save the file and complete this function.

| File name: | LATHE-LESSON-6 | ▾ |
| Save as type: | Mastercam X7 Files (*.MCX-7) | ▾ |

Toolpath Creation

TASK 9:
DEFINING THE STOCK AND CHUCK PARAMETERS

1. Fit the image to the screen by clicking on the Fit icon .
2. Then unzoom by clicking on the **Un-Zoom Previous / .5** icon as shown below:

3. Ensure your screen looks like the image below:
   a. The Toolpaths Manager is open, if it is not Select Alt and O on your keyboard to open it.
   b. The properties icon displays Lathe Default. If it is not refer to **Setting the Environment** chapter at the beginning of the book.
   c. The Lathe Lesson-6 Geometry is displayed.

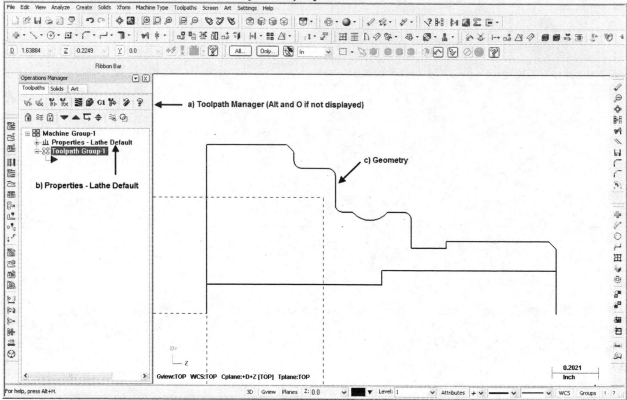

4. Select the plus in front of **Properties** to expand the Machine Group Properties.

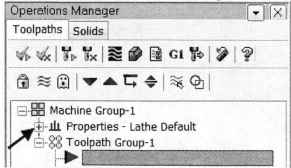

5. Select **Stock setup** in the Toolpaths Manager window.

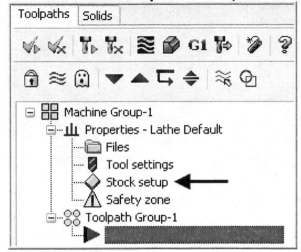

6. Select the **Stock Properties** button in the **Stock Setup** page as shown in the screenshot below:

Note:
To learn how to complete this section of the **Stock Setup** refer to the **Tips and Techniques** section on the **Mastercam Training Guide – Lathe DVD** that accompanies this book.

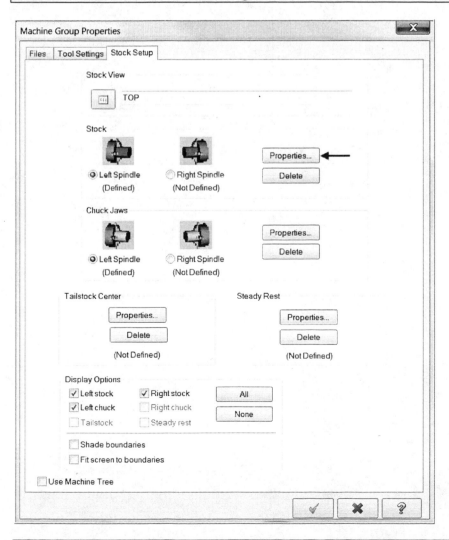

7. In the **Machine Component Manager-Stock** window click on the **Geometry** button and select **Cylinder** as shown below:

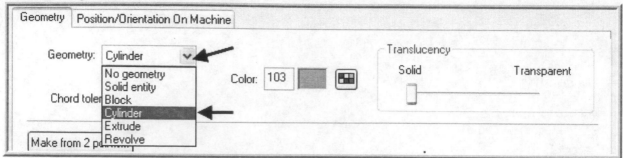

8. In the **Stock** setup set the values as shown below:

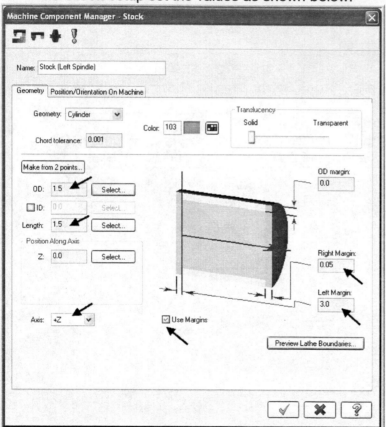

9. Click on the OK icon ✓ to complete this feature.

10. Select the **Chuck Properties** button in the **Stock Setup** page as shown in the screenshot below:

11. In the **Chuck Jaws** setup set the values as shown below:

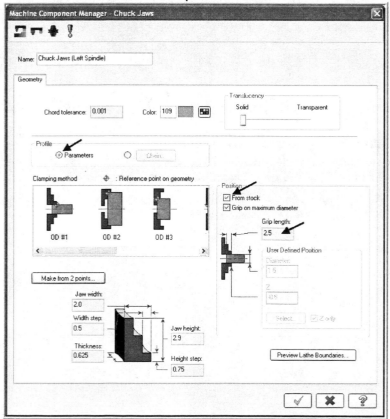

12. Click on the OK icon [✓] to complete this feature.

13. Click on the **Tool Settings** page and make changes as shown below:

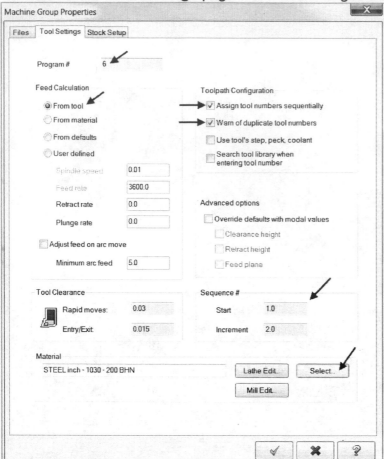

14. To change the **Material** type to Aluminium 6061 pick the **Select** button at the bottom of the Tool Settings page.
15. At the **Material List** dialog box open the Source drop down list and select **Lathe – library.**

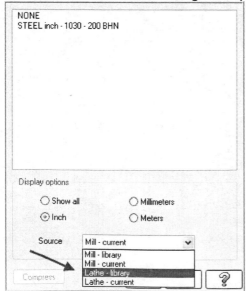

16. From the **Default Materials** list select **ALUMINIUM inch - 6061** and then select .

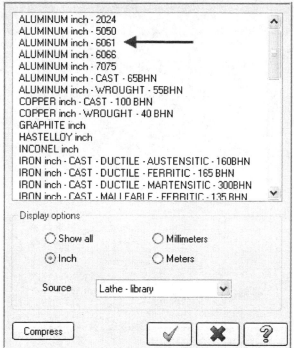

17. Select the OK button [✓] again to complete this Stock Setup function.
18. Zoom out by clicking on the **Un-Zoom Previous / .5** icon

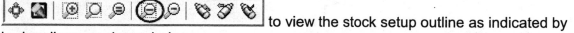 to view the stock setup outline as indicated by broken lines as shown below:

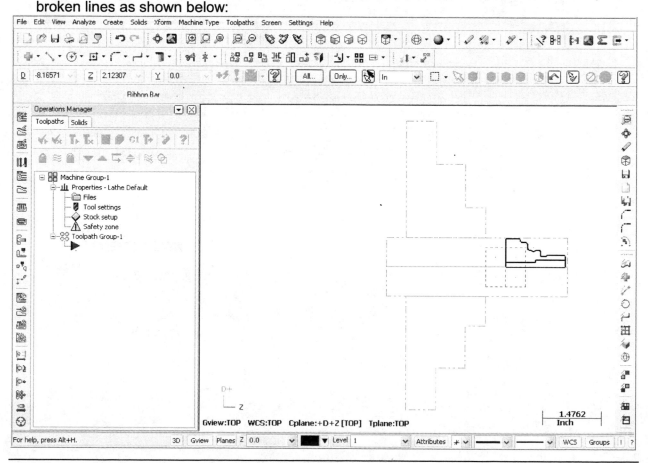

TASK 10:
FACE THE FRONT OF THE PART:

➲ In this task you will use a facing tool to face the front of the part in one cut.

1. Select the **Screen Fit** icon to fit the part to the screen ⊕.

2. Then select the **Un-Zoom previous / .5** icon. This function reduces the size of the displayed geometry to 50% of its current size.

3. From the menu bar select **Toolpaths>Face...**

4. When prompted to **"Enter new NC name"** Ensure **LATHE-LESSON-6** is entered as shown below and then select the OK button ✓.

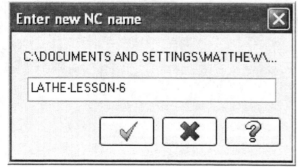

⊃ After selecting the OK button you are confronted with **Toolpath parameters** page. The first task here will be to select **Tool #1 a Roughing – 80 deg.**

5. Click on **Tool 0101 Roughing – 80 degree** and ensure the settings are the same as in the Toolpath parameters page as shown below:

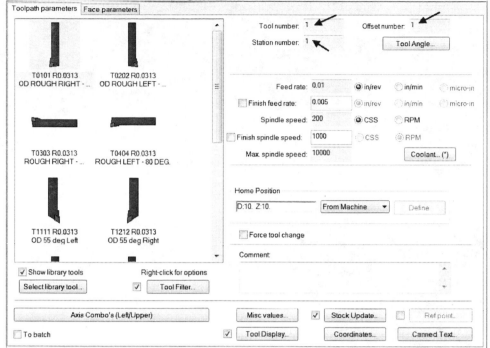

6. Select the **Face parameters** page and make changes as shown below:

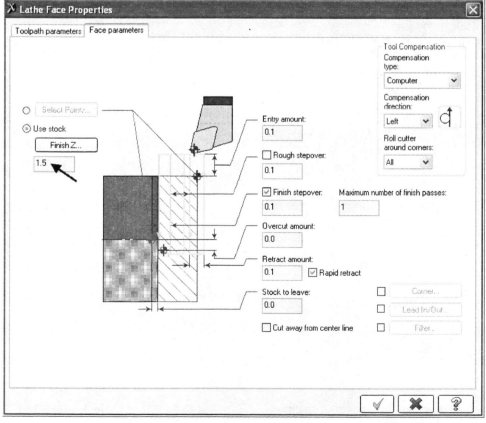

7. Select the OK button ☑ to complete this **Lathe Face** operation.

TASK 11:
ROUGH THE OUTSIDE DIAMETERS

➲ In this task you will use a Lathe toolpath called Lathe Quick Rough Toolpath.

➲ You will use the same tool as used for the previous facing operation **Tool #1 an OD Rough-Right – 80 deg.**

1. From the menu bar select **Toolpaths>Quick>Rough...**

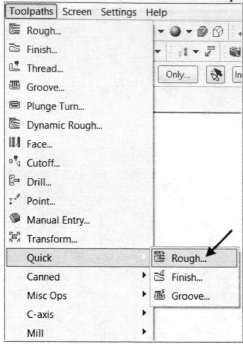

2. In the **Chaining** window Chaining mode is set to **Partial** by default.

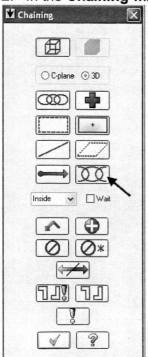

3. Select the chamfer, Line 1 as the start of the **Partial chain**.

After you have selected the chamfer **ensure** that the arrow is pointing towards the part as shown below. If it is not select the reverse button in the Chaining dialog box

4. Then select Line 2 as the end entity in this chain.

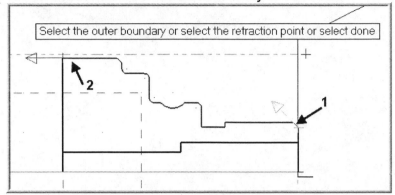

Select the outer boundary or select the retraction point or select done

5. Select the OK button ☑ to exit the Chaining dialog window.
6. In the **Quick Tool parameters** page select the **Tool #1 Roughing – 80 deg** and make any necessary changes as shown below:

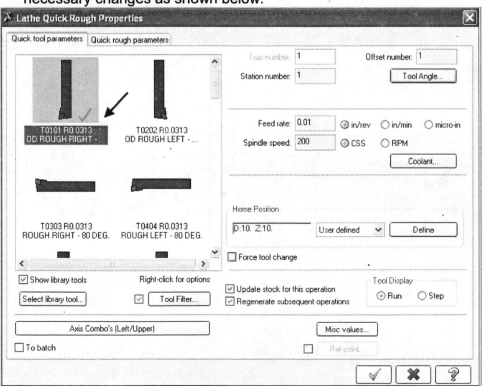

7. Select the **Quick Rough parameters** page and make any necessary changes as shown below:

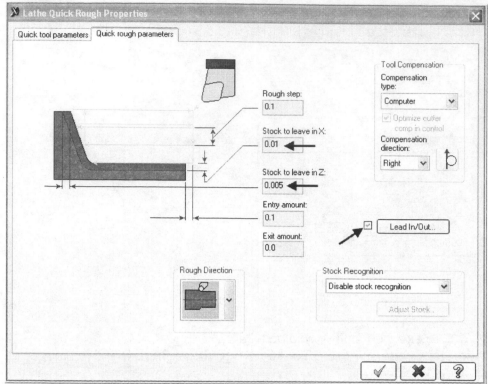

8. Select the **Lead In/Out** button, then select the **Lead out** page and extend the contour by .2 as shown below:

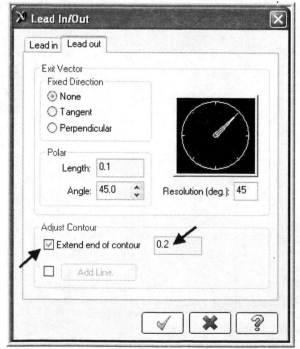

9. Select the OK button ✓ to exit this function.

10. Select the OK button ✓ to exit Quick Rough Parameters.

TASK 12:
FINISH THE OUTSIDE DIAMETERS
⮕ In this task you will finish the outside diameters using Quick Finish. The tool you used for rouging will be used in this operation as well.

1. From the menu bar select **Toolpaths>Quick>Finish...**

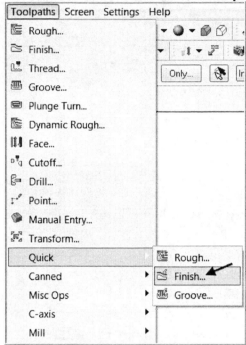

2. In the **Quick tool parameters** page select **Tool #1 Roughing – 80 deg** and make any necessary changes as shown below:

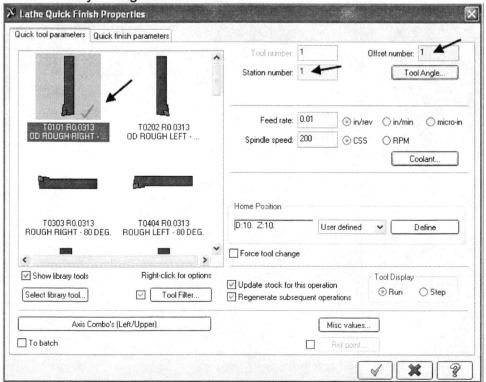

3. Select the **Quick finish parameters** page and make any necessary changes as shown below:

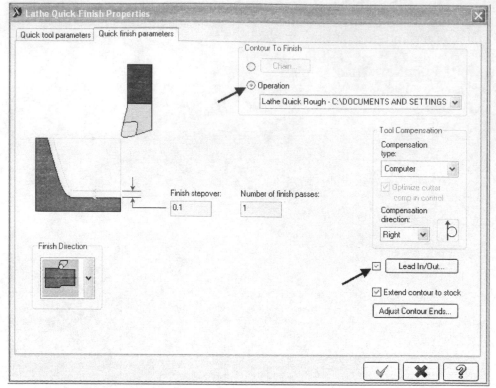

4. Select the **Lead In/Out** button select the Lead out page and extend the contour by **0.2** as shown below:

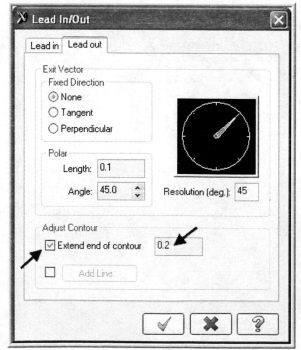

5. Select the OK button [✓] to exit this function.
6. Select the OK button [✓] to exit **Quick finish parameters**.

TASK 13:
FINISH THE 0.1 RADIUS
⊃ In this task you will create a new Tool to machine the **0.1" Radius**.

1. From the menu bar select **Toolpaths>Finish...**

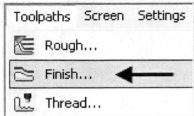

2. In the **Chaining** window click on the icon for Single
3. Select the **Arc** in the position shown below:

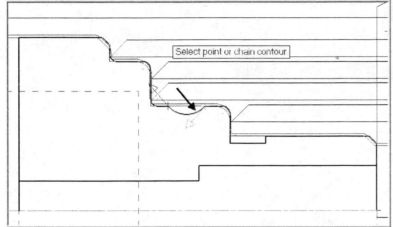

4. Select the OK button ☑ to exit the **Chaining** dialog window.
5. Right Click the mouse in the space as indicated by **arrow # 1** shown below:
6. Click on **Create new tool...** as indicated by **arrow # 2** as shown below:

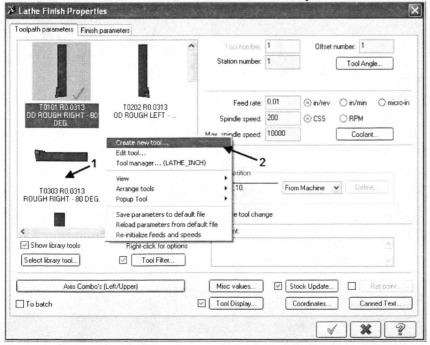

7. Click on the **General Turning** Button as shown below:

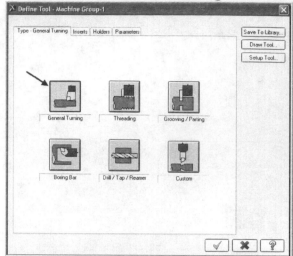

8. Click on the **Round** insert as shown below. Open up the drop down menu for **IC Dia / Length** and select **3/16**.

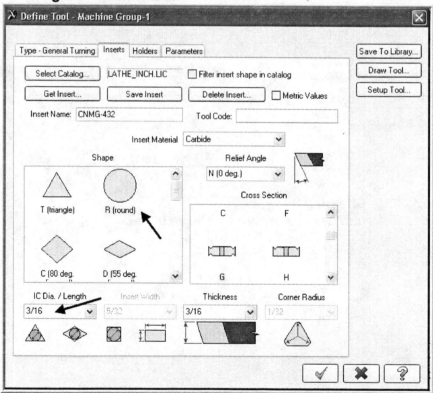

9. Click on the **Holders** Tab.
10. Scroll down and click on the **Offset Profiling** holder as shown below:

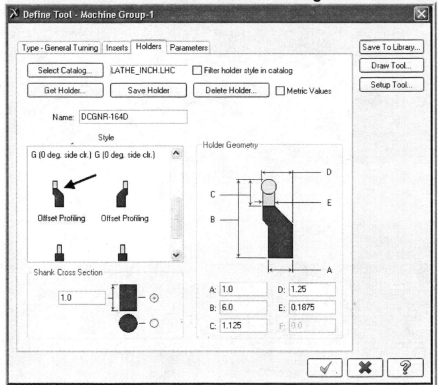

11. Click on the **Parameters** page and at the bottom of this page set the compensation for this tool as shown below:

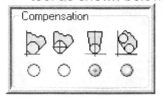

12. Click on the OK icon [✓].

13. Make any necessary changes on the **Toolpath parameters** page as shown below:

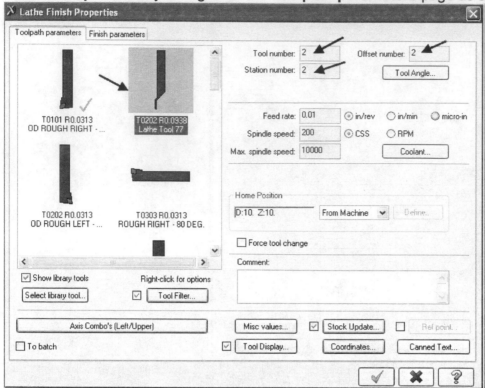

14. Click on the **Finish parameters** tab and make any necessary changes as shown below:

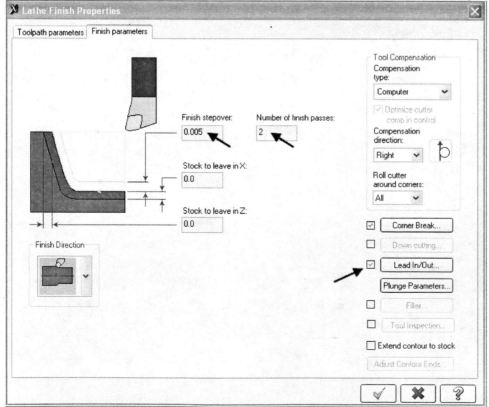

15. Click on the **Lead in/Out Button** as shown above:

16. Make the necessary changes as shown below on the **Lead In** page. In order to adjust the dial click on the desired location of the arrow:

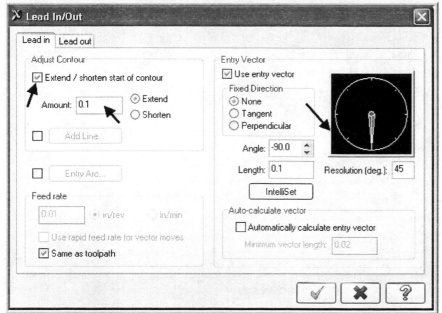

17. Click on the **Lead out** tab and make the necessary changes as shown below:

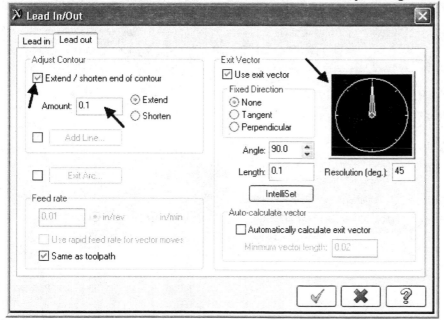

18. Click on OK [✓] to exit the Lead In/out window.

19. Click on the **Plunge Parameters** button [Plunge Parameters...].

20. Make the necessary changes as shown below:

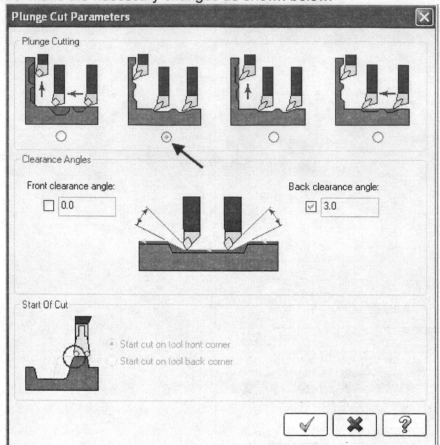

21. Click on Ok ✓ to exit the Plunge Cut Parameters window.

22. Click on Ok ✓ to exit the Lathe Finish parameters window.

TASK 14:
CENTER DRILL HOLE
➲ In this task you will center drill .2" depth using a **Centre Drill - .25 diameter.**

1. From the menu bar select **Toolpaths>Drill...**

2. Click on the **Select library tool** button 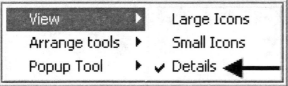 and then select the **Centre Drill .25 diameter.** To achieve the tool list view shown below, right mouse button click in the white space and select **View>Details**.

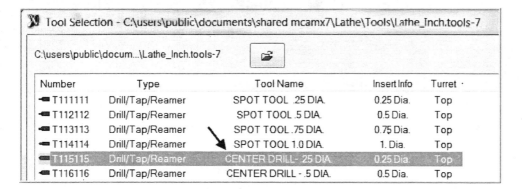

3. Select the OK button ☑ to exit the tool selection.

4. Make changes as shown below:

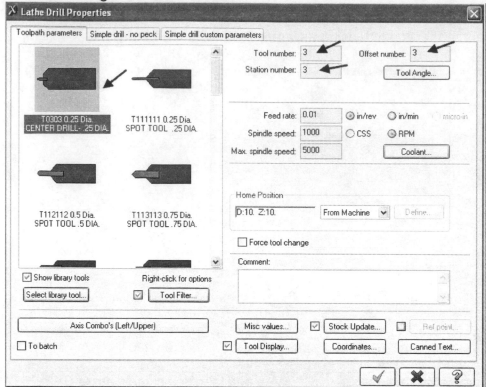

5. Select the **Simple drill** – no peck page and make changes as shown below:

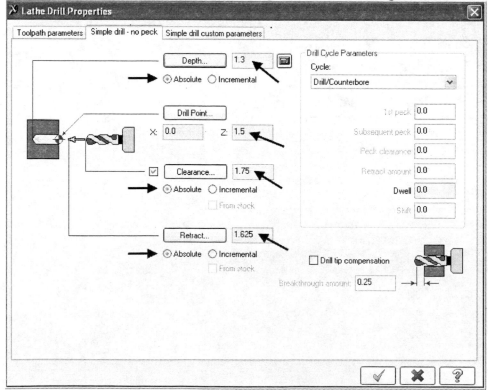

6. Select the OK button [✓] to exit **Simple drill – no peck**.

TASK 15:
PECK DRILL THE 0.250" HOLE
➲ In this task you will peck drill the 0.25" hole through the part using **Drill - .250 diameter**.

1. From the menu bar select **Toolpaths>Drill...**

2. Scroll down and select the **Drill - .250 diameter** tool from the tool list and make changes as shown below:

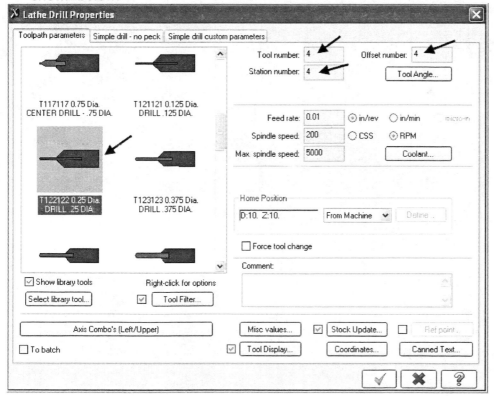

3. Select the **Simple drill – no peck** page and make changes as shown below. This hole will be **peck drilled through the part**. Make changes as shown below:

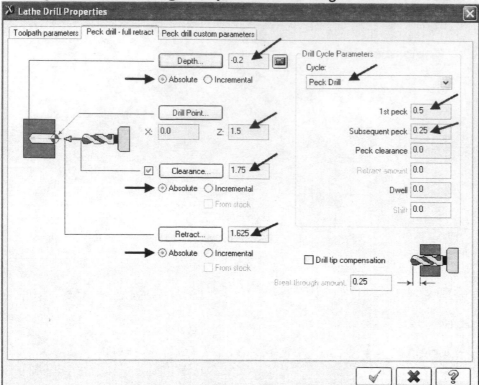

4. Select the OK button to exit Peck drill – full retract.

TASK 16:
DRILL THE 0.375" HOLE
⮕ In this task you will drill the 0.375" hole using **0.375 diameter end mill.**

1. From the menu bar select **Toolpaths>Drill...**

2. Scroll down and select the **0.375 DIA. - .007R diameter End Mill** tool from the tool list and make changes as shown below:

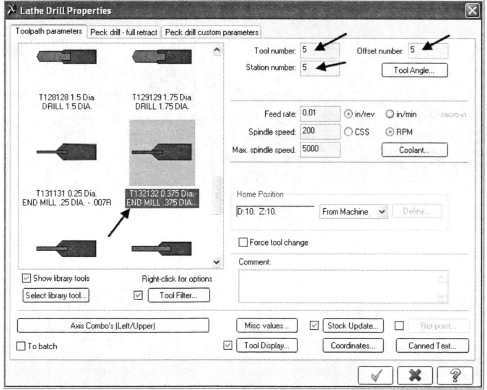

3. Select the second tab **Peck drill – full retract** and make changes as shown below. This is a **Simple drill – no peck** operation so change the **Cycle to Drill/Counterbore**.

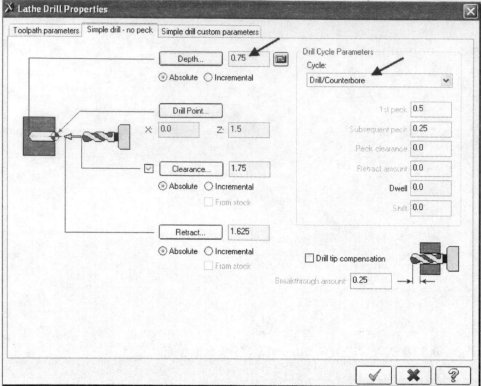

4. Select the OK button [✓] to exit Simple drill – no peck.

TASK 17:
CUT THE GROOVE

➲ In this task you will use the Lathe Groove toolpath using an **OD Groove Right Width .125.**
1. From the menu bar select **Toolpaths>Groove...**

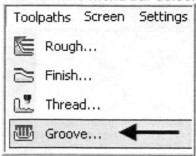

2. The Grooving Options window appears. Click on the **Chain** option as shown below:

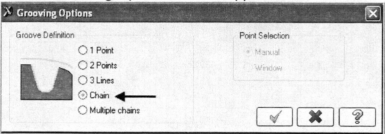

3. Click on OK [✓].
4. Select **Alt and T** on the keyboard to hide the toolpath.
5. Zoom in on the groove area as shown below:
6. In the **Chaining** window Chaining mode is set to **Partial** by default.
7. Select **Line 1** as the start of the **Partial chain**.

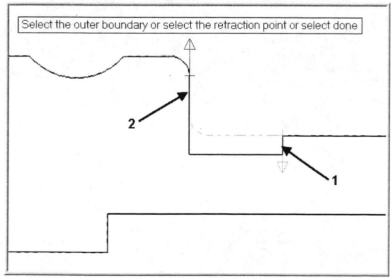

After you have selected line 1 **ensure** that the arrow is pointing downwards If it is not select the reverse button in the Chaining dialog box

8. Then select **Line 2** as the end entity in this chain.

9. Select the OK button [✓] to exit the Chaining dialog window.
10. Select **OD Groove Right Width .125** tool from the tool list and make any necessary changes as shown below:

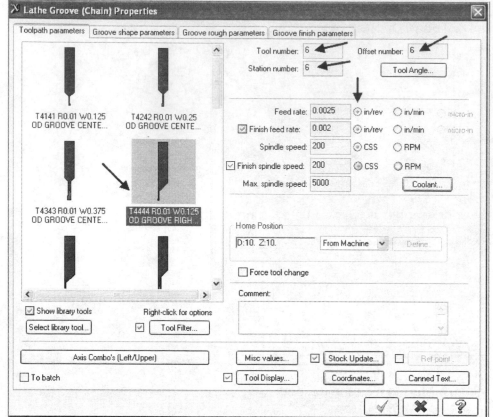

11. Select the **Groove finish parameters** page.

12. Click on the Lead **In** button [Lead In...] and make changes to the **Second pass Lead in** page as shown below.

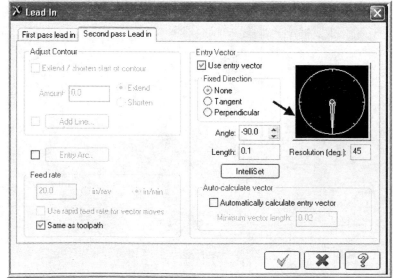

13. Select the OK button [✓] to exit Lead in.
14. Select the OK button [✓] to exit as no further changes are required.

TASK 18:
CUT OFF THE PART

⊃ In this task you will cut off the part using **OD Groove Right Width .125** the same tool as the previous grooving operation.

1. Fit the image to the screen by clicking on the **Fit** icon as shown below:

2. Then unzoom by clicking on the **Un-Zoom Previous / .5** icon as shown below:

3. From the menu bar select **Toolpaths>Cutoff...**

4. When prompted to **Select cutoff boundary point** pick the end point of the line shown below. Move the cursor over the corner until the visual cue for End point displays and then click on this point.

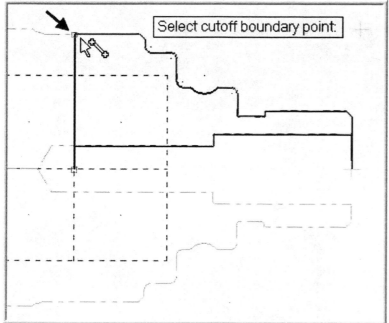

5. Select **OD GROOVE RIGHT WIDTH .125** tool from the tool list and make any necessary changes as shown below:

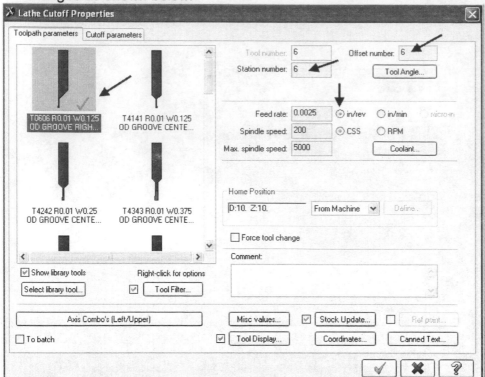

6. Select the **Cutoff parameters** page and make sure the settings are as shown below:

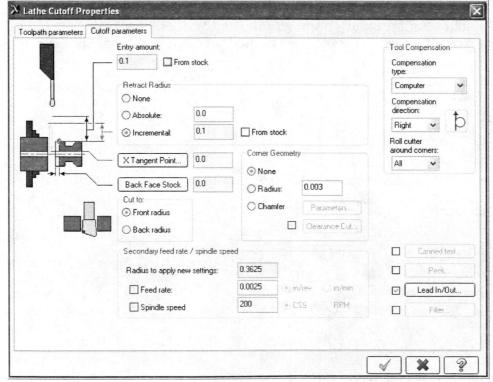

7. Select the OK button [✓] to exit **Lathe Cutoff parameters.**

TASK 19:
VERIFY THE TOOLPATH

➲ Mastercam's Verify utility allows you to use solid models to simulate the machining of a part. The model created by the verification represents the surface finish, and shows collisions, if any exist.

1. In the Toolpaths Manager pick all the operations to backplot by picking the **Select All** icon

2. Select the **Verify selected operations** icon shown below:

   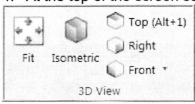

3. **Maximize** the Backplot/Verify window if required.
4. At the top of the screen select the **Isometric** icon and then select **Fit**.

   ```
   ┌─────────────────────────────────┐
   │  ↔     ⬡      ◇  Top (Alt+1)    │
   │                                  │
   │                  ⬡  Right        │
   │  Fit   Isometric                 │
   │                  ⬡  Front ▾      │
   │                                  │
   │          3D View                 │
   └─────────────────────────────────┘
   ```

5. Activate the options shown below in the **Visibility** section of the Home tab. **Initial Stock not activated.**

   ```
   ┌─────────────────────────────────┐
   │  ☐ Toolpath    ✓ Stock          │
   │  ✓ Tool        ☐ Initial Stock  │
   │  ☐ Workpiece   ✓ Fixtures       │
   │        Visibility                │
   └─────────────────────────────────┘
   ```

6. In the lower right corner of the screen now set the run **Speed** to slow by moving the slider bar pointer over to the left as shown below.

   ```
   ┌─────────────────────────────────┐
   │  Speed:  ▯━━━━━━━━━━━━━          │
   │          ┆┆┆┆┆┆┆┆┆┆┆┆┆          │
   └─────────────────────────────────┘
   ```

7. Now select the **Play Simulation** button to review the toolpaths.

8. Select the Close button [X] in the top right hand corner to exit Verify.

TASK 20:
SAVE THE UPDATED MASTERCAM FILE

File   Edit   View   /

1. Select the save icon from the toolbar

TASK 21:
POST AND CREATE THE CNC CODE FILE

1. Ensure all the operations are selected by picking the **Select All** icon  from the Toolpaths manager.

2. Select the **Post selected operations** button from the Toolpaths manager.
➲ **Please Note:** If you cannot see **G1** click on the right pane of the Toolpaths manager window and expand the window to the right.

3. In the Post processing window, make the necessary changes as shown below:

About Post Processing

NC file:
Select this option to save the NC file. The file name and extension are stored in the machine group properties for the selected operation. If you are posting operations from different machine groups or Mastercam files, or batch processing, Mastercam will create several files according to the settings for each machine group.

Edit:
When checked, automatically launches the default text editor with the file displayed so that you can review or modify it.

4. Select the OK button ✓ to continue.

5. Ensure the same name as your Mastercam part file name is displayed in the **NC File name** field.
6. Select the **Save** button.
7. The CNC code file opens up in the default editor.

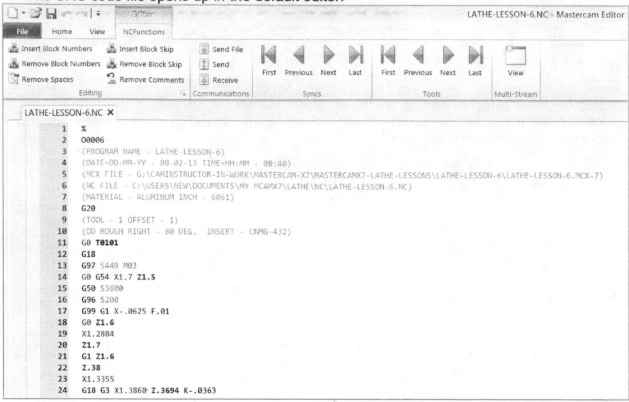

8. Select the ☒ in the top right corner to exit the CNC editor.
9. This completes LATHE-LESSON-6.

LATHE-LESSON-6 EXERCISE

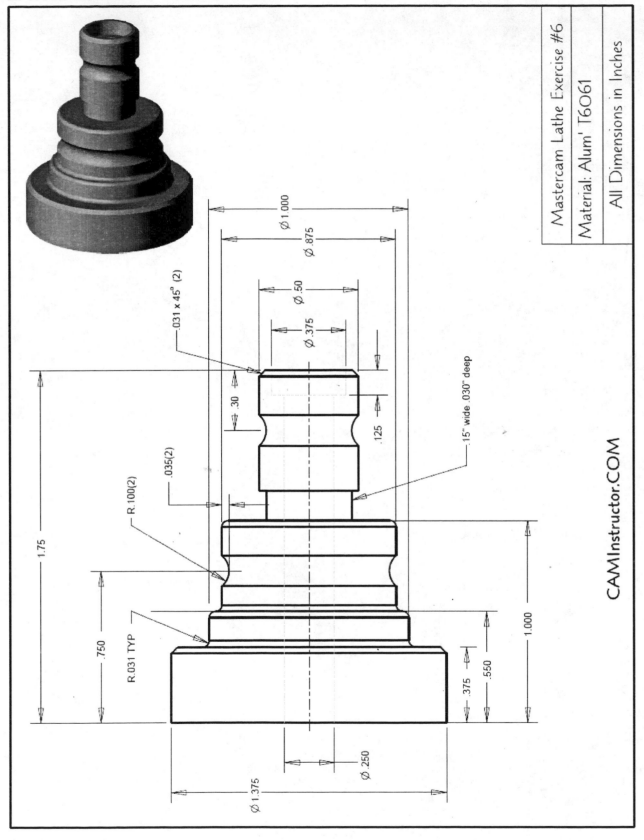

Mastercam Lathe Exercise #6

Material: Alum' T6O61

All Dimensions in Inches

Ø 1.000
Ø .875
Ø .50
Ø .375
.031 x 45° (2)
.30
.125
.15" wide .030" deep
.035(2)
R.100(2)
1.75
.750
R.031 TYP
1.000
.375
.550
Ø .250
Ø 1.375

CAMInstructor.COM

Mastercam X⁷

Training Guide

Lathe-Lesson-7

Face, Quick Rough and Finish, Drill, Tap, Groove and Cutoff

camInstructor

Objectives

You will create the geometry for Lathe Lesson-7, and then generate a toolpath to machine the part on a CNC lathe. This lesson covers the following topics:

⊃ Create a 2-dimensional drawing by:
Creating lines.
Creating fillets.
Creating chamfers.
Trimming geometry.

⊃ Establish Stock and Chuck Setup settings:
Stock size.
Chuck Configuration.
Material for the part.
Feed calculation.

⊃ Generate a 2-dimensional lathe toolpath consisting of:
Lathe Face.
Lathe Quick Rough.
Lathe Quick Finish.
Lathe Finish.
Lathe Drill.
Lathe Groove.
Lathe Cutoff.

⊃ Inspect the toolpath using Mastercam's Verify and Backplot by:
Launching the Verify function to machine the part on the screen.
Generating the NC- code.

LATHE - LESSON-7 DRAWING

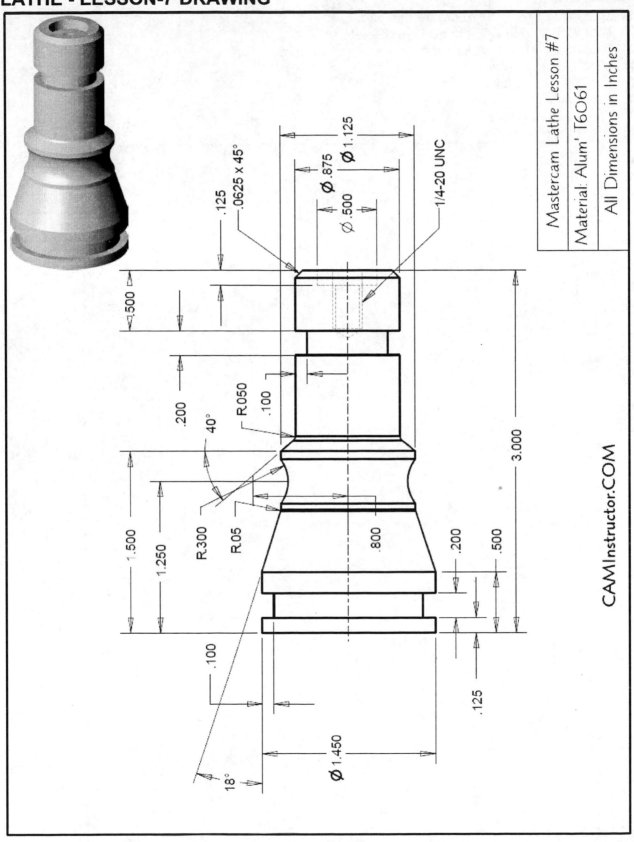

Mastercam Lathe Lesson #7

Material: Alum' T6061

All Dimensions in Inches

CAMInstructor.COM

TOOL LIST

Seven tools will be used to create this part.
- ➲ Tool #1 Face, Rough the outside diameters
- ➲ Tool #2 Finish the outside diameters
- ➲ Tool #3 Center drill
- ➲ Tool #4 13/64 diameter drill
- ➲ Tool #5 ¼-20 UNC tap
- ➲ Tool #6 Boring tool
- ➲ Tool #7 Cutoff tool

```
        Tool List of LATHE-LESSON-7.MCX-5

  Proj./Part No.: 0                Date       : 06/24/10
  Drawing No.   : 1                Customer   : -
  Prog. No.     : 7                Programmer : 1
```

```
        Tool type     : T0101: specific tool type - OD ROUGH RIGHT - 80 DEG.
        Manufact.code :
        Holder/Insert : DCGNR-164D / CNMG-432
        Setup length  :
        Spindle RPM   :    200      Feedrate UPR :    0.01     Corner radius :    0.0313
        Length offset :      1      Tool chan. D,Z:     14   ,     8
```

```
        Tool type     : T0202: specific tool type - OD FINISH RIGHT - 35 DEG.
        Manufact.code :
        Holder/Insert : MVJNR-164D / VNMG-431
        Setup length  :
        Spindle RPM   :    200      Feedrate UPR :    0.005    Corner radius :    0.0156
        Length offset :      2      Tool chan. D,Z:     14   ,     8
```

```
        Tool type     : T0303: specific tool type - CENTER DRILL- .25 DIA.
        Manufact.code :
        Holder/Insert : /
        Setup length  :
        Spindle RPM   :   1000      Feedrate UPR :    0.01     Corner radius :       0
        Length offset :      3      Tool chan. D,Z:     10   ,    10
```

```
        Tool type     : T0404: specific tool type - 13/64 DRILL
        Manufact.code :
        Holder/Insert : 13/64 DRILL / 13/64 DRILL
        Setup length  :
        Spindle RPM   :   1316      Feedrate UPM :    4.2126   Corner radius :       0
        Length offset :      4      Tool chan. D,Z:     10   ,    10
```

```
        Tool type     : T0505: specific tool type - 1/4-20 RH TAP
        Manufact.code :
        Holder/Insert : 1/4-20 RH TAP / 1/4-20 RH TAP
        Setup length  :
        Spindle RPM   :   1069      Feedrate UPM :   53.48     Corner radius :       0
        Length offset :      5      Tool chan. D,Z:     10   ,    10
```

```
        Tool type     : T0606: specific tool type - ID ROUGH MIN. .1875 DIA. - 75 DEG.
        Manufact.code :
        Holder/Insert : /
        Setup length  :
        Spindle RPM   :    200      Feedrate UPR :    0.01     Corner radius :    0.0078
        Length offset :      6      Tool chan. D,Z:     14   ,     8
```

```
        Tool type     : T0707: specific tool type - OD GROOVE RIGHT - NARROW
        Manufact.code :
        Holder/Insert : / GC-4125
        Setup length  :
        Spindle RPM   :    200      Feedrate UPR :    0.01     Corner radius :    0.01
        Length offset :      7      Tool chan. D,Z:     14   ,     8
```

LESSON - 7 - THE PROCESS

Geometry Creation

TASK 1:   Setting the environment
TASK 2:   Setting the construction planes
TASK 3:   Create the geometry – Part 1
TASK 4:   Create the geometry – Part 2
TASK 5:   Create the 40 degree line and 0.050 fillets
TASK 6:   Create the chamfer on right side of part
TASK 7:   Create the 0.300" Radius
TASK 8:   Trim the Geometry
TASK 9:   Create the geometry for the bore
TASK 10:   Trim the geometry for the bore
TASK 11:   Save the drawing

Toolpath Creation

TASK 12:   Define the stock and chuck parameters
TASK 13:   Face the front of the part
TASK 14:   Rough the outside diameters
TASK 15:   Finish the outside diameters
TASK 16:   Finish the 0.3 radius
TASK 17:   Center drill hole
TASK 18:   Tap Drill 13/64" diameter
TASK 19:   Tap the ¼-20 UNC Hole
TASK 20:   Rough the bore
TASK 21:   Finish the bore
TASK 22:   Cut the Grooves
TASK 23:   Cut off the part
TASK 24:   Verify the toolpath
TASK 25:   Save the updated Mastercam file
TASK 26:   Post and create the cnc code file

Geometry Creation

TASK 1:
SETTING THE ENVIRONMENT

Before starting the geometry creation you should set up the grid and toolbars as outlined in the **Setting the Environment** section at the beginning of this text:
1. Set up the Grid. This will help identify the location of the origin.
2. Customize the toolbars to machine a part on the Lathe.
3. Set the machine type to the default Lathe.

TASK 2:
SETTING THE CONSTRUCTION PLANES:

⮕ **Set the Construction Plane to Lathe diameter +D +Z (WCS)**
1. Click on Planes at the bottom of the screen as shown below:

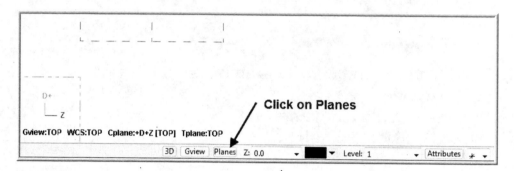

2. Click on Lathe diameter>+D +Z (WCS) as shown below:

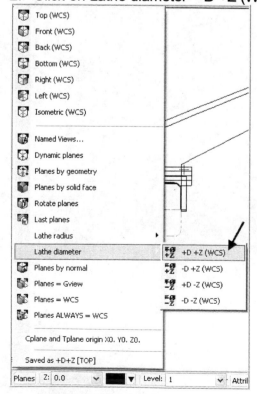

TASK 3:
CREATE THE GEOMETRY – PART 1
⮞ This task explains how to create the geometry of this part. In this lathe part you only need to create half of the geometry, the geometry above the center line.
⮞ Lines 1 through 8 will be created in this task.

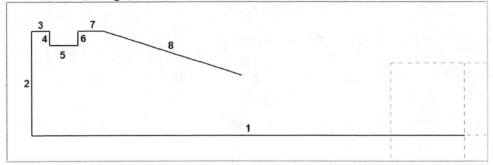

⮞ **Create Line #1**
1. Select **Alt-O** on your keyboard to turn off the display of the Toolpaths Manager.
2. Select from the pull down menu **Create>Line>Endpoint…**

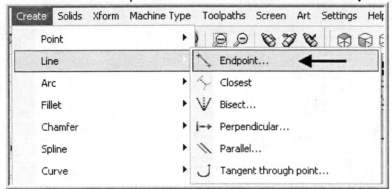

3. The Line ribbon bar appears:

4. Move the cursor over the **center of the grid** and as you get close to the origin a visual cue

   appears. This is the cue that will allow you to snap to the **origin**. With this visual cue highlighted pick the **origin**.
5. You are next prompted to **"Specify the second endpoint"**. On the left hand side of the Line ribbon bar click on the **Multi-Line** button to activate it as shown below by the arrow:

6. Click in the **D** value space (Diameter) and enter a value of **0**. Hit the Enter key and enter a value of **-3.0 for the Z**, hit the Enter key again and enter a value of **0 for the Y** and hit Enter.

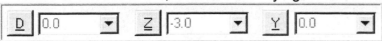

➲ **Create Line #2**

7. Click in the D value space (Diameter) and enter a value of **1.45**. Hit the Enter key and enter a value of **-3.0 for the Z**, hit the Enter key again and enter a value of **0 for the Y** and hit Enter.

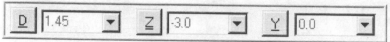

8. Fit the image to the screen by clicking on the Fit icon as shown below:

➲ **Create Line #3**

9. **"Specify the second endpoint"**; Type in **1.45 in D** hit Enter, type in **-3.0+0.125 in Z** and hit Enter and type in **0.0 in Y** and hit Enter.

➲ **Create Line #4**

10. **"Specify the second endpoint"**; Type in **1.450-0.2 in D** hit Enter, type in **-3.0+0.125 in Z** and hit Enter and type in **0.0 in Y** and hit Enter.

➲ **Create Line #5**

11. **"Specify the second endpoint"**; Type in **1.450-0.2 in D** hit Enter, type in **-3.0+0.125+0.2** in Z and hit Enter and type in **0.0 in Y** and hit Enter.

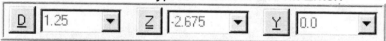

➲ **Create Line #6**

12. **"Specify the second endpoint"**; Type in **1.45 in D** hit Enter, type in **-3.0+0.125+0.2 in Z** and hit Enter and type in **0.0 in Y** and hit Enter.

➲ **Create Line #7**

13. **"Specify the second endpoint"**; Type in **1.45 in D** hit Enter, type in **-3.0+0.500 in Z** and hit Enter and type in **0.0 in Y** and hit Enter.

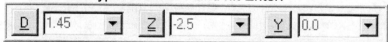

➲ **Create Line #8**

14. Now click in the space for **Length** and enter a value of **1.0** and hit the tab key to move over to Angle.
15. In the space for **Angle** enter a value of **-18.0** and hit the enter key.

16. Click on the OK icon ✓ to complete this feature.

TASK 4:
CREATE THE GEOMETRY – PART 2
➜ This task explains how to create the geometry of this part.
➜ Lines 9 through 15 will be created using **Line>Parallel**.

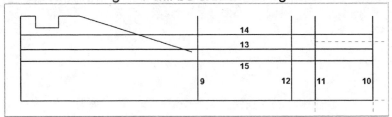

1. Fit the image to the screen by clicking on the **Fit** icon as shown below:

2. Your geometry should look like the figure below:

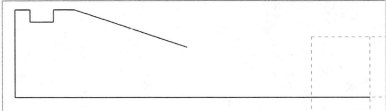

➜ **Create Line #9**
3. Select from the pull down menu: **Create>Line>Parallel....**
4. On the graphics screen you are prompted **"Select a line"** and the Line Parallel ribbon bar appears.
5. To satisfy the prompt **Select a line**, select the line shown below:

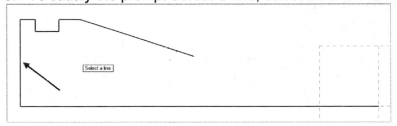

6. To satisfy the next prompt **Select the point to place a parallel line through** move the cursor to the right of the line and pick a point.
7. For the **Distance** input **1.500** then hit **enter**.

8. On the ribbon bar click on **Apply** ⊕ to fix the entity.

⊃ **Create Line #10**

9. To satisfy the prompt **Select a line**, select the line shown below:

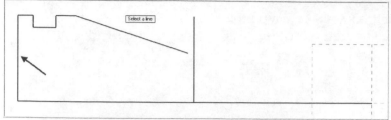

10. To satisfy the next prompt **Select the point to place a parallel line through** move the cursor to the right of the line and pick a point.
11. For the **Distance** input **3.0** then hit **enter.**

12. On the ribbon bar click on **Apply** to fix the entity.

⊃ **Create Line #11**

13. To satisfy the prompt **Select a line**, select the line shown below:

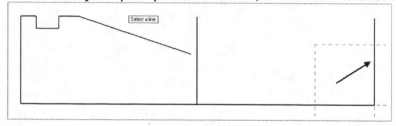

14. To satisfy the next prompt **Select the point to place a parallel line through** move the cursor to the left of the line and pick a.point.
15. For the **Distance** input **0.500** then hit **enter**

16. On the ribbon bar click on **Apply** to fix the entity.

⊃ **Create Line #12**

17. To satisfy the prompt **Select a line**, select the line shown below:

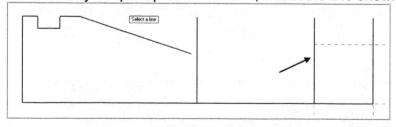

18. To satisfy the next prompt **Select the point to place a parallel line through** move the cursor to the left of the line and pick a point.
19. For the **Distance** input **0.200** then hit **enter.**

20. On the ribbon bar click on **Apply** to fix the entity.

➲ **Create Line #13**

21. To satisfy the prompt **Select a line**, select the line shown below:

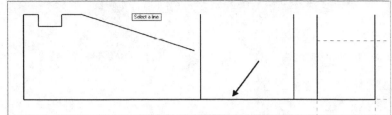

22. To satisfy the next prompt **Select the point to place a parallel line through** move the cursor above the line and pick a point.

23. For the **Distance** input **0.875/2** then hit **enter**.

24. On the ribbon bar click on **Apply** to fix the entity.

➲ **Create Line #14**

25. To satisfy the prompt **Select a line**, select the line shown below:

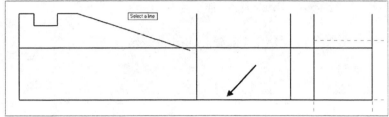

26. To satisfy the next prompt **Select the point to place a parallel line through** move the cursor above the line and pick a point.

27. For the **Distance** input **1.125/2** then hit **enter**.

28. On the ribbon bar click on **Apply** to fix the entity.

➲ **Create Line #15**

29. To satisfy the prompt **Select a line**, select the line shown below:

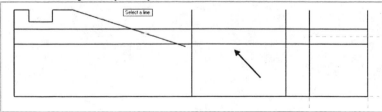

30. To satisfy the next prompt **Select the point to place a parallel line through** move the cursor below the line and pick a point.

31. For the **Distance** input **0.1** then hit **enter**.

32. Click on the **OK** icon to complete this feature. Completed geometry is shown below:

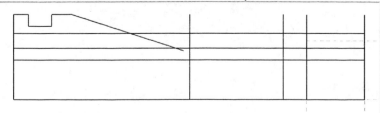

TASK 5:
CREATE THE 40 DEGREE LINE AND 0.050 FILLETS

1. Select from the pull down menu **Create>Line>Endpoint...**

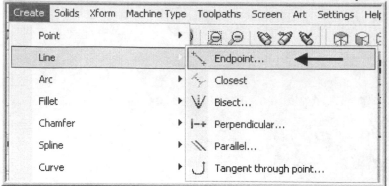

2. You are next prompted to **"Specify the first endpoint"**. Move the cursor over the

   intersection of the two lines shown below and when the visual cue for intersection appears pick this point.

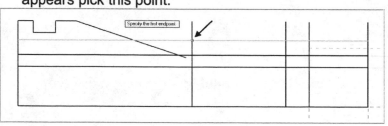

3. Now click in the space for **Length** and enter a value of **0.25** and hit the tab key to move over to Angle value.
4. For **Angle** enter a value of **-50.0 (90-40 degrees)** and hit the enter key.

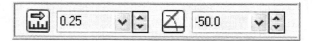

5. Click on the **OK** icon to complete this feature.

Your geometry should look like the figure below:

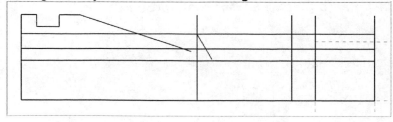

○ **Create 0.050 fillet**

6. Select **Create>Fillet>Entities...**

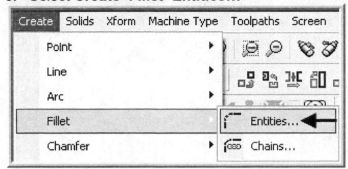

7. On the Fillet ribbon bar enter **0.050 for the radius** and hit enter. Ensure the **Style** of radius is set to **Normal** and the trim button is depressed to turn the **trim on**.

8. When prompted to **Fillet: Select an entity,** select Line 1 and 2 as shown below:
9. When prompted to **Fillet: Select an entity,** select Line 3 and 4 as shown below:

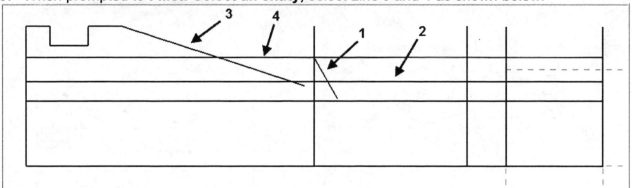

10. Click on the **OK** icon ☑ to complete this feature. The completed geometry is shown below:

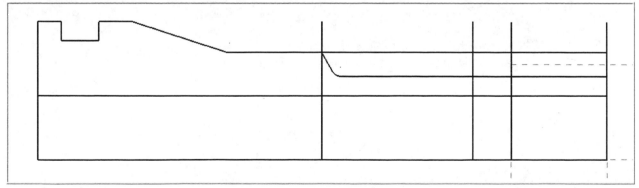

TASK 6:
CREATE THE CHAMFER ON RIGHT SIDE OF PART
➔ Create the chamfer 45 degrees x .0625.

1. Select **Create>Chamfer>Entities...**

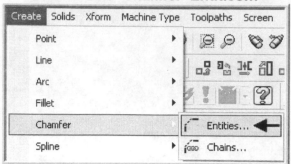

2. You are prompted to Select line or arc .
3. Click in the **Distance** window as shown below and type in **0.0625** and hit enter:

4. Ensure the **1 Distance** option is selected and **Trim is on** as shown above:
5. Click on line 1 and then line 2 as shown below on the right side of the part.

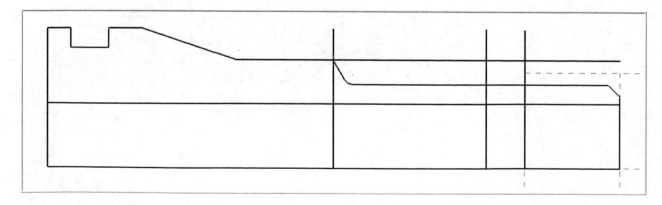

6. Click on the **OK** icon [✓] to complete this feature.
7. The completed geometry should look like the image below:

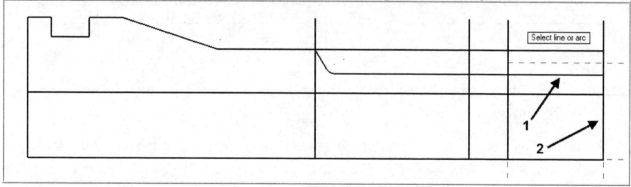

TASK 7:
CREATE THE 0.300" RADIUS
➲ In this task you will create the 0.300 arc. The center position and radius are known.

1. Select **Create>Arc>Arc Polar...**

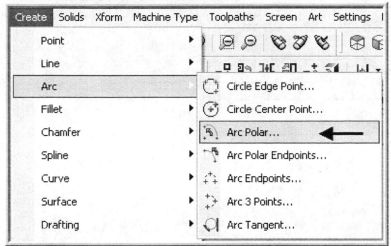

2. The **Arc Polar** ribbon bar appears and you are prompted to **Enter the center point** click on the **FastPoint** icon as shown below and enter the coordinates for the center of the arc **1.600 , -1.75** and then hit enter.

3. The prompt now changes to **Sketch the initial angle**. Click in the space for **radius** and enter **0.3** and then hit the **tab key twice** to move over to the start angle.
4. Input a **Start angle of 0** and hit the tab key.
5. For the **End angle** input **180** and then hit enter. Use the **Flip** button to place the arc in the desired position as shown below.

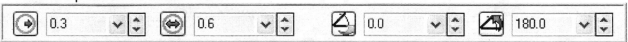

6. Click on the **OK** icon to complete this feature.
7. The completed arc is shown below:

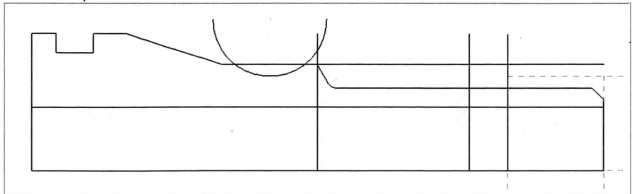

TASK 8:
TRIM THE GEOMETRY
➲ In this task you will use **Divide** to trim the entities.

1. **Delete** the line shown below: Select the line and hit the delete key on your keyboard.

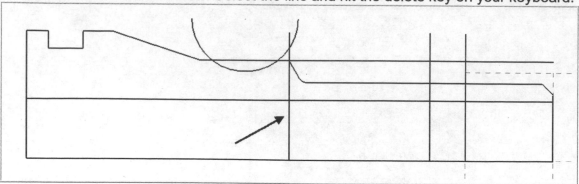

2. Select **Edit>Trim/Break>Trim/Break/Extend**
3. The Trim / Extend / Break ribbon bar appears and you are prompted to **Select the entity to trim/extend**.
4. Now click on the **Divide** icon [+·+].
5. The prompt changes to **Select the curve to divide.** Move the cursor over the various entities and select in the order and position shown below:

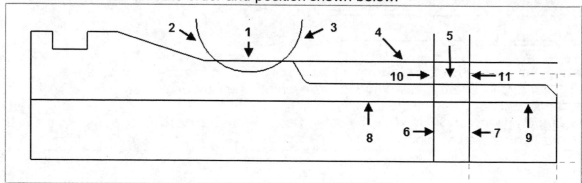

6. Click on the **OK** icon [✓] to complete this feature.
7. **Delete** the three lines shown below: Select the three lines and then hit the delete key on your keyboard.

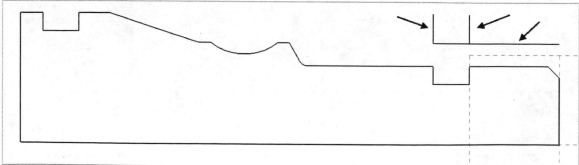

TASK 9:
CREATE THE GEOMETRY FOR THE BORE

➲ In this task you will create the geometry that make up the bore of this part
1. Select from the pull down menu: **Create>Line>Parallel....**
2. On the graphics screen you are prompted **"Select a line"** and the Line Parallel ribbon bar appears.
3. To satisfy the prompt **Select a line**, select the line shown below:

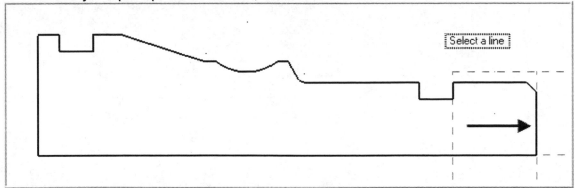

4. To satisfy the next prompt **Select the point to place a parallel line through** move the cursor to the left of the line and pick a point.
5. For the **Distance** input **0.125** then hit **enter**.

6. On the ribbon bar click on **Apply** to fix the entity.
7. To satisfy the prompt **Select a line**, select the line shown below:

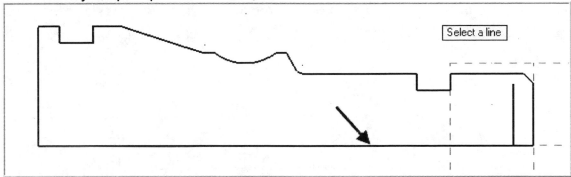

8. To satisfy the next prompt **Select the point to place a parallel line through** move the cursor above the line and pick a point.
9. For the **Distance** input **0.500/2** then hit **enter.**

10. On the ribbon bar click on **Apply** to fix the entity,
11. To satisfy the prompt **Select a line**, select the line shown below:

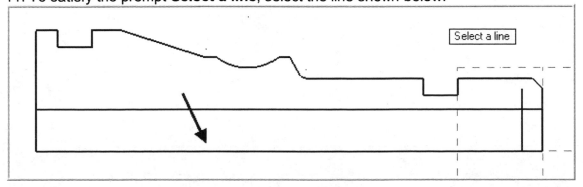

12. To satisfy the next prompt **Select the point to place a parallel line through** move the cursor above the line and pick a point.
13. For the **Distance** input **0.250/2** then hit **enter.**
14. Click on the **OK** icon ✓ to complete this feature. The completed geometry is shown below:

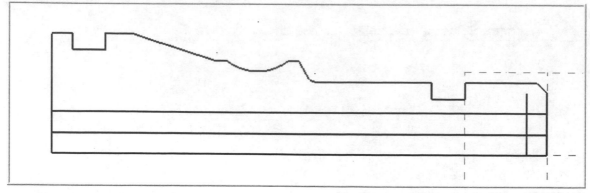

TASK 10:
TRIM THE GEOMETRY FOR THE BORE

1. Select **Edit>Trim/Break>Trim/Break/Extend**
2. The Trim / Extend / Break ribbon bar appears and you are prompted to **Select the entity to trim/extend.**
3. Now click on the **Divide** icon ⊢┼┤.
4. The prompt changes to **Select the curve to divide.** Move the cursor over the various entities and select in the order and position shown below:

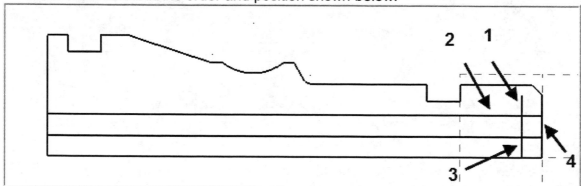

5. Click on the **OK** icon ✓ to complete this feature.
6. **Delete** the three lines shown below: Select the three lines and then hit the delete key on your keyboard.

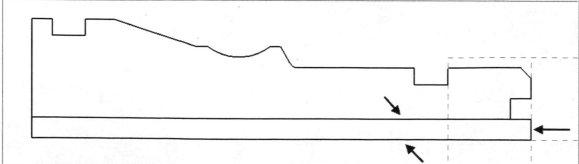

7. The completed geometry is shown below:

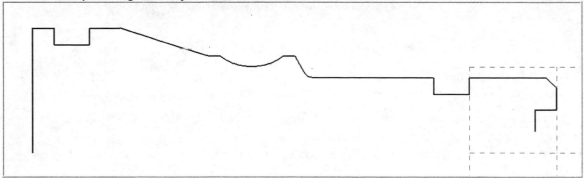

TASK 11:
SAVE THE DRAWING

1. Select **File.**
2. Select **Save as.**
3. In the **"File name"** box, type **"Lathe-Lesson-7".**
4. Save to an appropriate location.
5. Select the Save button to save the file and complete this function.

File name: LATHE-LESSON-7

Save as type: Mastercam X7 Files (*.MCX-7)

Toolpath Creation

TASK 12:
DEFINING THE STOCK AND CHUCK PARAMETERS

1. Fit the image to the screen by clicking on the **Fit** icon ⬙.
2. Then unzoom by clicking on the **Un-zoom Previous / .5** icon as shown below:

3. Ensure your screen looks like the image below:
   a. The **Toolpaths Manager** is open, if it is not Select **Alt and O** on your keyboard to open it.
   b. The properties icon displays Lathe Default. If it is not refer to **Setting the Environment** chapter at the beginning of the book.
   c. The **Lathe Lesson-7** Geometry is displayed.

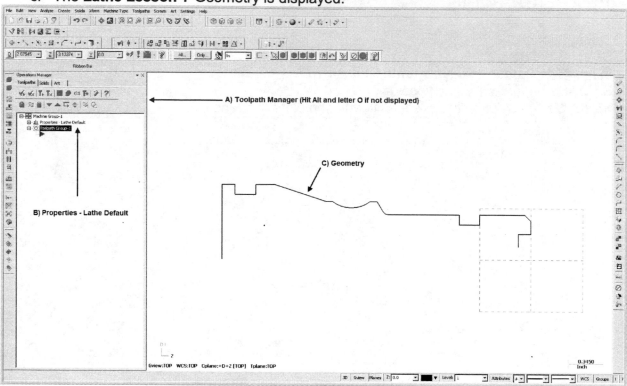

4. Select the plus in front of **Properties** to expand the Machine Group Properties.

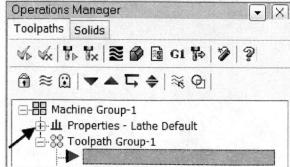

5. Select **Stock setup** in the Toolpaths Manager window.

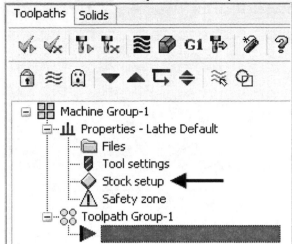

6. Select the **Stock Properties** button in the **Stock Setup** page as shown in the screenshot below:

> ➲ Note: To learn how to complete this section of the **Stock Setup** refer to the Tips and Techniques section on the **Mastercam Training Guide – Lathe DVD** that accompanies this book.

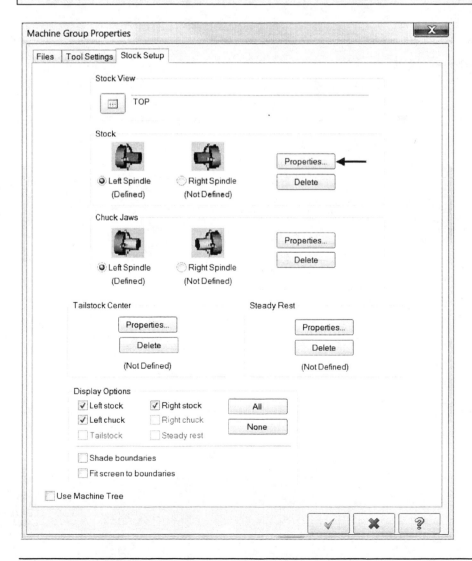

7. In the **Machine Component Manager-Stock** window click on the **Geometry** button and select **Cylinder** as shown below:

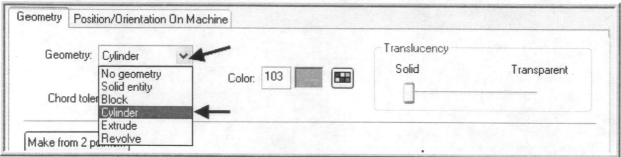

8. In the **Stock setup** set the values as shown below:

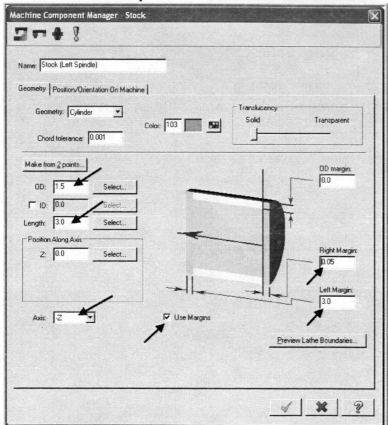

9. Click on the OK icon [✓] to complete this feature.

10. Select the **Chuck Properties** button in the **Stock Setup** page as shown in the screenshot below:

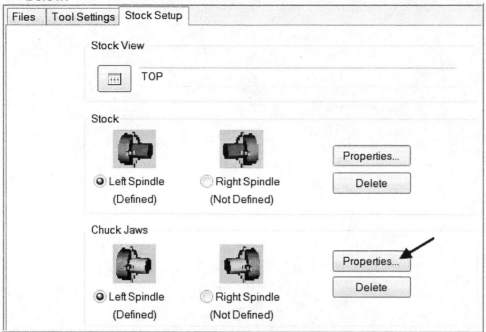

11. In the **Chuck Jaws** setup set the values as shown below:

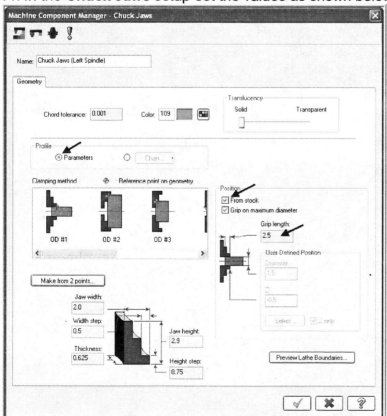

12. Click on the OK icon to complete this feature.

13. Click on the **Tool Settings** page and make changes as shown below:

14. To change the **Material** type to Aluminium 6061 pick the **Select** button at the bottom of the Tool Settings page.

15. At the **Material List** dialog box open the Source drop down list and select **Lathe – library.**

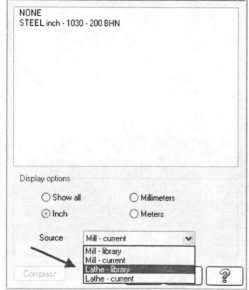

16. From the **Default Materials** list select **ALUMINIUM inch - 6061** and then select .

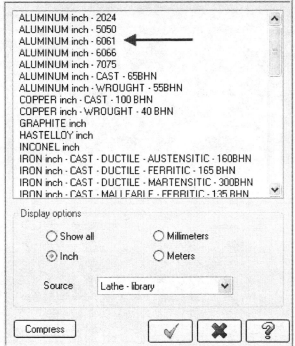

17. Select the **OK** button 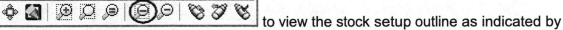 again to complete this Stock Setup function.
18. Zoom out by clicking on the **Un-Zoom Previous / .5** icon

to view the stock setup outline as indicated by broken lines as shown below:

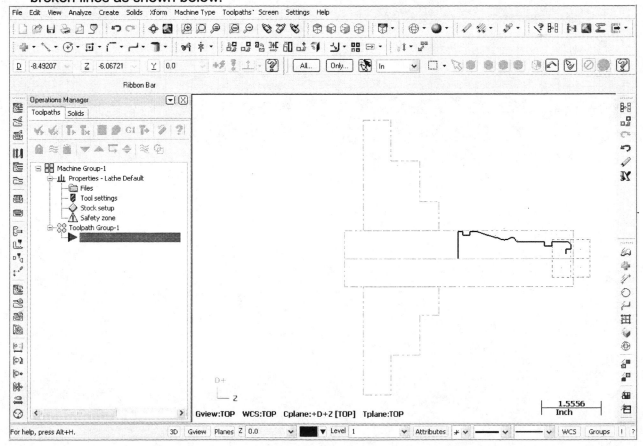

TASK 13:
FACE THE FRONT OF THE PART:

➲ In this task you will use a facing tool to face the front of the part in one cut.

1. Select the **Screen Fit** icon to fit the part to the screen [⬥].

2. Then select the **Un-zoom previous / .5** icon. [icon] This function reduces the size of the displayed geometry to 50% of its current size.

3. From the menu bar select **Toolpaths>Face...**

4. When prompted to **"Enter new NC name"** Ensure **LATHE-LESSON-7** is entered as shown below and then select the **OK** button [✓].

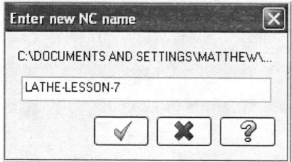

➲ After selecting the **OK** button you are confronted with **Toolpath parameters** page. The first task here will be to select **Tool #1 a Roughing – 80 deg.**

5. Click on **Tool 0101 Roughing – 80 degree** and ensure the settings are the same as in the Toolpath parameters page as shown below:

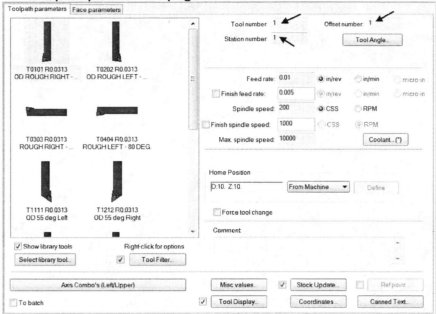

6. Select the **Face parameters** page and make changes as shown below:

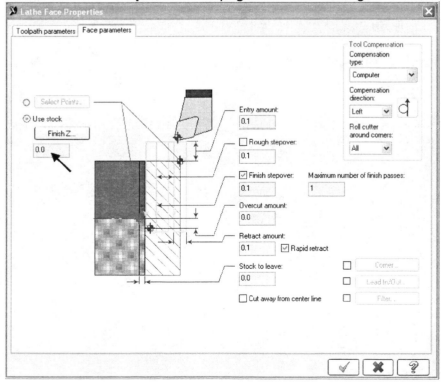

7. Select the **OK** button ✓ to complete this **Lathe Face** operation.

TASK 14:
ROUGH THE OUTSIDE DIAMETERS
- ⊃ In this task you will use Lathe Quick Rough Toolpath to rough the outside diameters.
- ⊃ You will use the same tool as used for the previous facing operation Tool #1 an OD Rough-Right – 80 deg.

1. From the menu bar select **Toolpaths> Quick> Rough...**

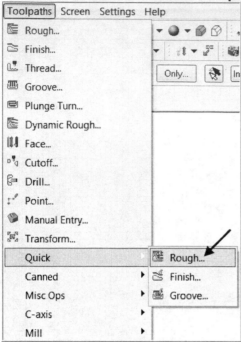

2. In the Chaining window Chaining mode is set to Partial by default.

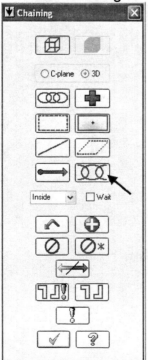

3. Select the chamfer, Line 1 as the start of the Partial chain.

After you have selected the chamfer **ensure** that the arrow is pointing towards the part as shown below: If it is not select the reverse button in the Chaining dialog box

4. Then select Line 2 as the end entity in this chain.

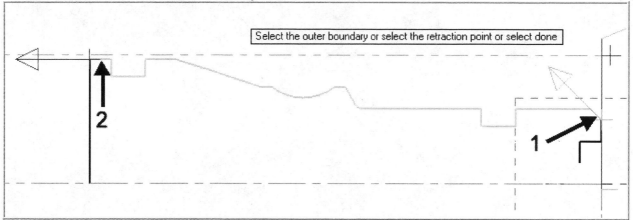

5. Select the OK button 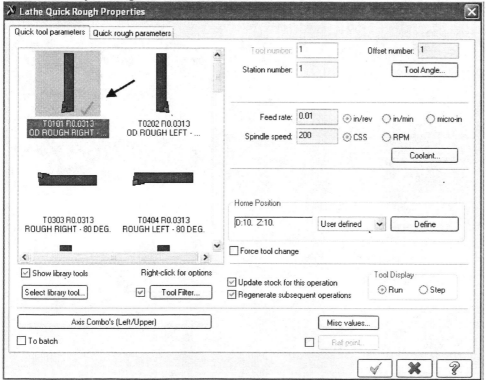 to exit the Chaining dialog window.
6. In the Quick Toolpath parameters page select the Tool #1 Roughing – 80 deg and make any necessary changes as shown below:

7. Select the **Quick Rough** parameters page and make any necessary changes as shown below:

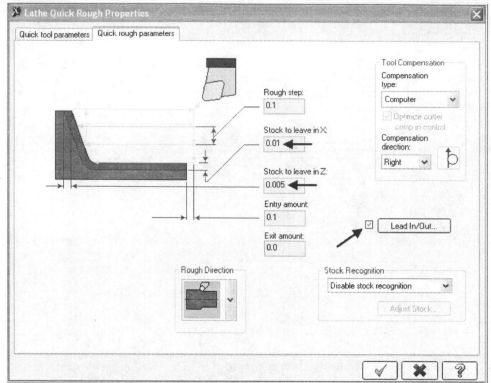

8. Select the **Lead In/Out** button, then select the **Lead out** page and extend the contour by .2 as shown below:

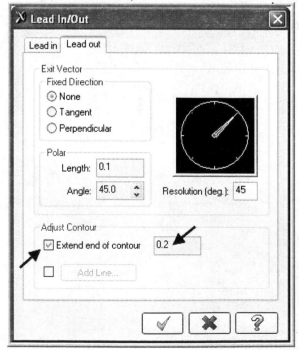

9. Select the **OK** button [✓] to exit this function.

10. Select the **OK** button [✓] to exit Quick Rough Parameters.

TASK 15:
FINISH THE OUTSIDE DIAMETERS

⮠ In this task you will finish the outside diameters using Lathe Quick Finish Toolpath. The tool will be Tool #2 Finish – 35 deg.

1. From the menu bar select **Toolpaths>Quick>Finish...**

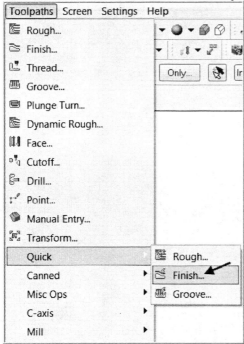

2. In the Quick tool parameters page **scroll down and locate the tool: OD Finish Right – 35 deg. Then double click on this tool.**

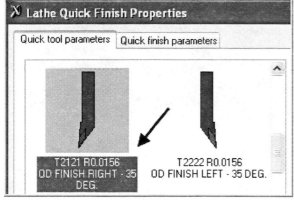

3. Click on the **Parameters** page and at the bottom of this page set the compensation for this tool as shown below:

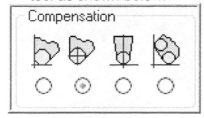

4. Click on the **OK** icon [✓].

5. Back in the **Toolpath parameters** page make any necessary changes as shown below:

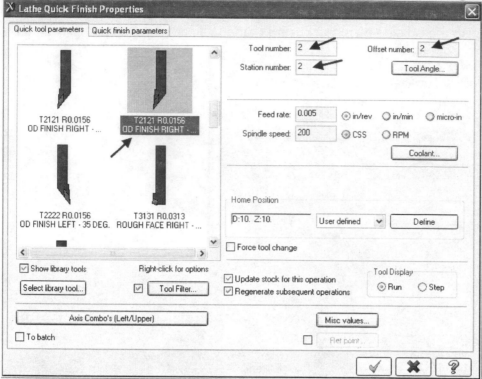

6. Select the **Quick Finish** parameters page and make any necessary changes as shown below:

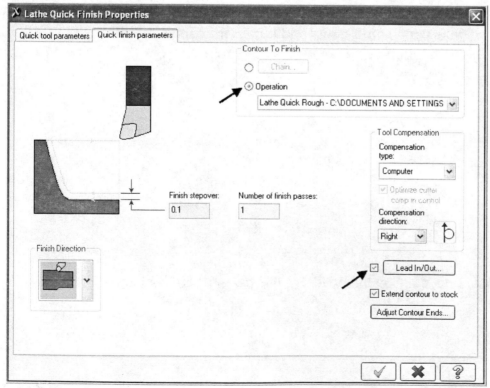

7. Select the **Lead In/Out** button select the **Lead out** page and extend the contour by .2 as shown below:

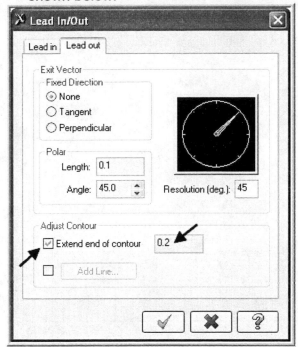

8. Select the **OK** button [✓] to exit this function.
9. Select the **OK** button [✓] to exit **Quick finish parameters**.

TASK 16:
FINISH THE 0.3 RADIUS

⮕ In this task you will finish the 0.3 radius using the same tool you used for finishing a **Tool #2 Finish – 35 deg**.

1. From the menu bar select **Toolpaths>Finish...**

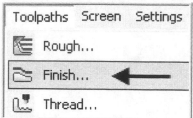

2. In the **Chaining** window click on the icon for **Single**
3. Select the Arc in the position shown below

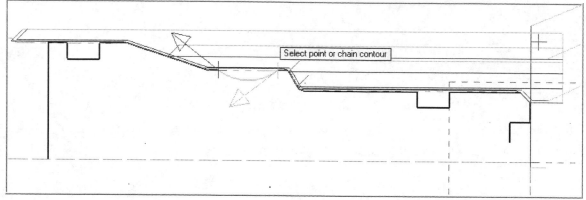

4. Select the **OK** button [✓] to exit the Chaining dialog window.
5. In the **Toolpath parameters** page select **Tool #2 Finish – 35 deg** and make any necessary changes as shown below:

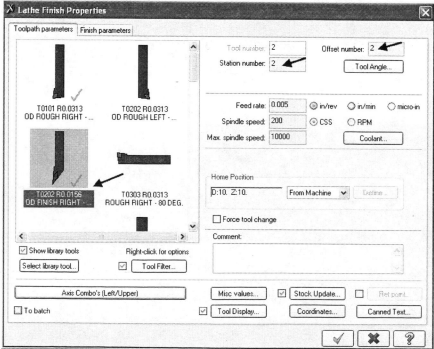

6. Click on the **Finish parameters** tab and make any necessary changes as shown below:

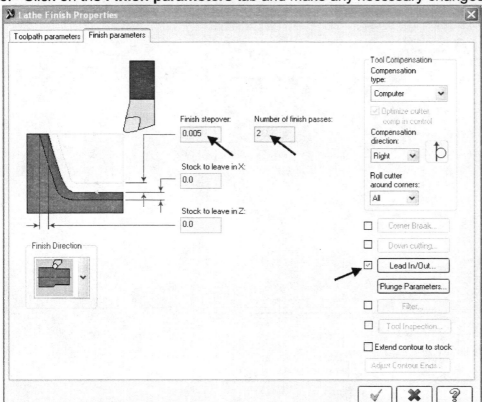

7. Click on the **Lead in/Out** button as shown above:
8. Make the necessary changes as shown below on the **Lead In** page. In order to adjust the dial click on the desired location of the arrow:

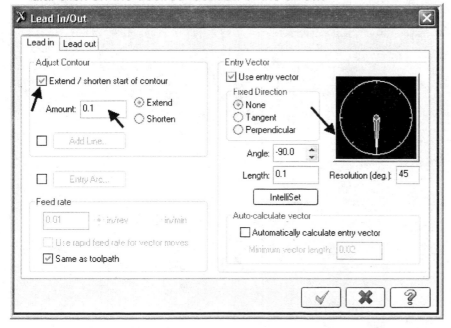

9. Click on the **Lead out** tab and make the necessary changes as shown below:

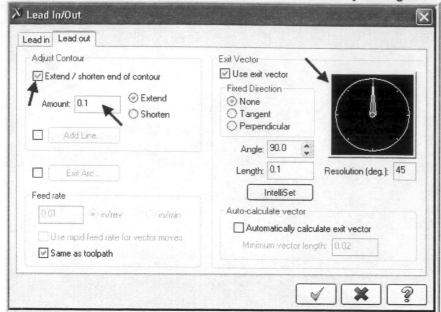

10. Click on **OK** ☑ to exit the Lead In/out window.

11. Click on the **Plunge Parameters** button [Plunge Parameters...]

12. Make the necessary changes as shown below:

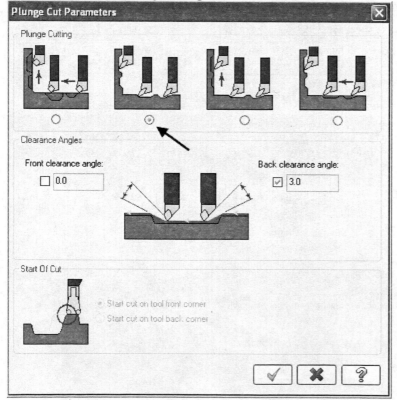

13. Click on Ok ☑ to exit the **Plunge Cut** Parameters window.

14. Click on Ok ☑ to exit the **Lathe Finish** parameters window.

TASK 17:
CENTER DRILL HOLE

➲ In this task you will center drill .2" depth using a **Centre Drill - .25 diameter.**

1. From the menu bar select **Toolpaths>Drill...**

2. Click on the **Select library tool** button [Select library tool...] and then select the **Centre Drill .25 diameter.** To achieve the tool list view shown below, right mouse button click in the white space and select **View>Details.**

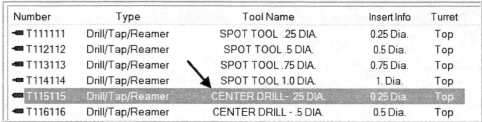

Number	Type	Tool Name	Insert Info	Turret
T111111	Drill/Tap/Reamer	SPOT TOOL .25 DIA.	0.25 Dia.	Top
T112112	Drill/Tap/Reamer	SPOT TOOL .5 DIA.	0.5 Dia.	Top
T113113	Drill/Tap/Reamer	SPOT TOOL .75 DIA.	0.75 Dia.	Top
T114114	Drill/Tap/Reamer	SPOT TOOL 1.0 DIA.	1. Dia.	Top
T115115	Drill/Tap/Reamer	CENTER DRILL- .25 DIA.	0.25 Dia.	Top
T116116	Drill/Tap/Reamer	CENTER DRILL - .5 DIA.	0.5 Dia.	Top

3. Select the **OK** button [✓] to exit the tool selection.

4. Make changes as shown below:

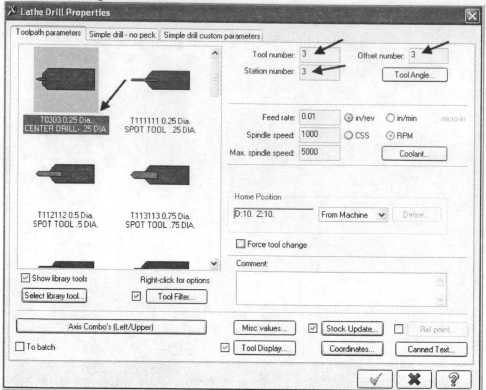

5. Select the **Simple drill – no peck** tab and make changes as shown below:

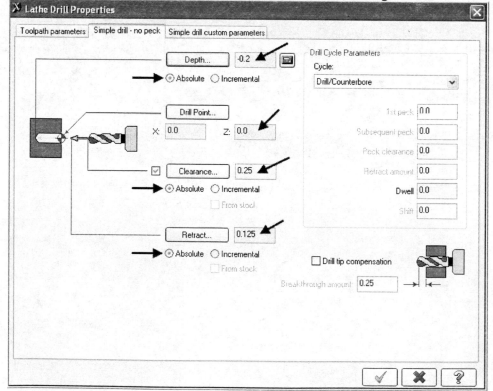

6. Select the **OK** button ✓ to exit **Simple drill – no peck**.

TASK 18:
TAP DRILL THE 0.25-20 UNC TAPPED HOLE 13/64 DIAMETER
⮑ In this task you will tap drill the 0.25-20 UNC hole using **13/64 diameter drill** this will be a peck drill operation.

1. From the menu bar select **Toolpaths>Drill...**

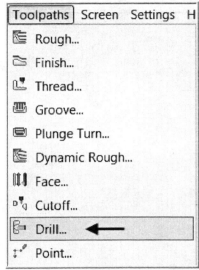

2. At the **Toolpath** parameters page click on the Select library tool button Select library tool... .

3. At the top left of this dialog box open up the Select new folder icon to show the library tools list and select **LDRILLS.**

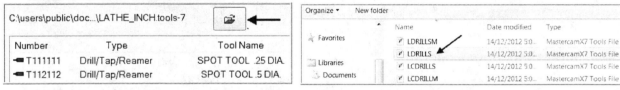

4. Scroll down and select the **13/64 drill** from the list:

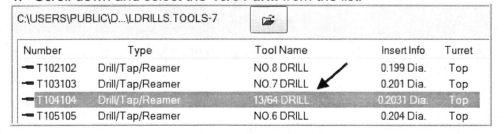

5. Select the **OK** button ✓ to exit the tool selection.
6. Select the **OK** button for the Duplicate tool numbers warning if it appears.

7. Make changes as shown below:

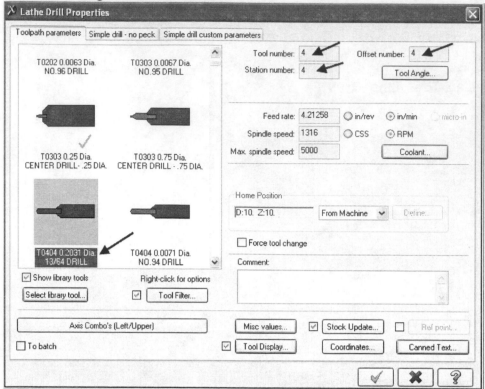

8. Select the **Simple drill – no peck** page and make changes as shown below: This hole will be peck drilled so **select the Cycle as Peck Drill** Make changes as shown below:

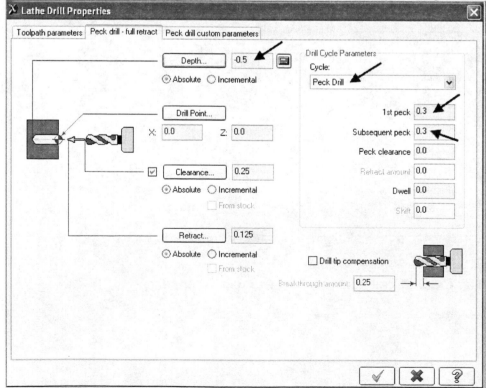

⊃   As the drawing specifies the depth of 0.5 from the front face at full diameter you will now use the **Depth calculator** to calculate the true depth, taking into account the tip angle of this drill.

9. Click on the **Depth calculator** icon.
10. At the Depth Calculator dialog box activate the radio button for **Add to depth**.

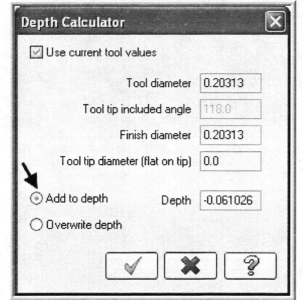

Use the **Depth Calculator** to calculate the proper drilling depth when the finish diameter of the hole is different from the drill diameter— for example, when countersinking a hole. Mastercam automatically displays the **Tool diameter**, **Tool tip included angle**, and **Tool tip diameter** for the drill that has been selected for the operation. Deselect **Use current tool values** to specify different values for these parameters.
Once you calculate the depth, you have two options:
Choose **Overwrite depth** to replace the existing depth value on the parameter page.
Choose **Add to depth** to add the calculated depth to the existing depth value on the parameter page.

11. Select the **OK** button to exit Depth Calculator.
12. Notice how now the depth has been changed,

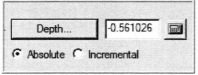

13. Select the **OK** button to exit Peck drill – full retract.

TASK 19:
TAP THE 0.25-20 UNC TAPPED HOLE
➲ In this task you will tap the 0.25-20 hole.

1.   From the menu bar select **Toolpaths>Drill...**

2.   At the Toolpath parameters page click on the **Select library** tool button [Select library tool...].

3.   Select the **select new folder** icon  at the top of the dialog box and then the **LTAPS** from the list as shown below:

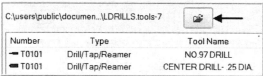

Organize ▾	New folder		
	Name	Date modified	Type
Favorites	✓ LTAPSM	14/12/2012 5:0...	MastercamX7 Tools File
Libraries	✓ LTAPS	14/12/2012 5:0...	MastercamX7 Tools File
	✓ LREAMERS	14/12/2012 5:0...	MastercamX7 Tools File

4.   Select the **1/4-20 RH TAP** from the list:

Number	Type	Tool Name	Insert Info	Turret
T1919	Drill/Tap/Reamer	NO.12-24 RH TAP	0.216 Dia.	Top
T2020	Drill/Tap/Reamer	NO.12-28 RH TAP	0.216 Dia.	Top
T2121	Drill/Tap/Reamer	1/4-20 RH TAP	0.25 Dia.	Top

5.   Select the **OK** button [✓] to exit the tool selection.

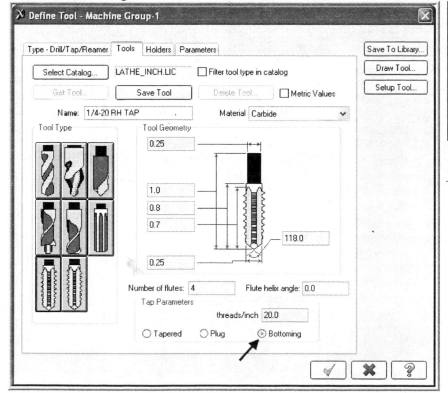

6. **Double** click on the **1/4-20 tap** in the **Tool parameters** page.

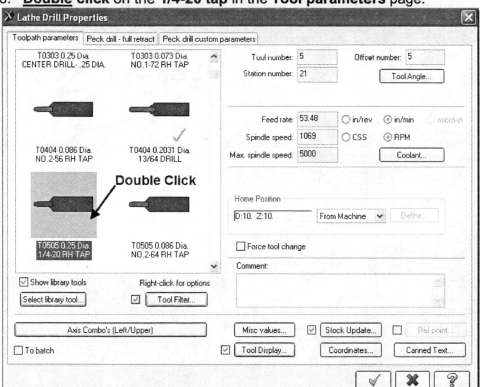

7. At the lower right corner of the screen activate the radio button for **Bottoming**.

> **Bottoming**
> Select this option if you want the tap to have the same diameter all the way down.
> This type of tap is used to cut threads through the bottom of the hole.

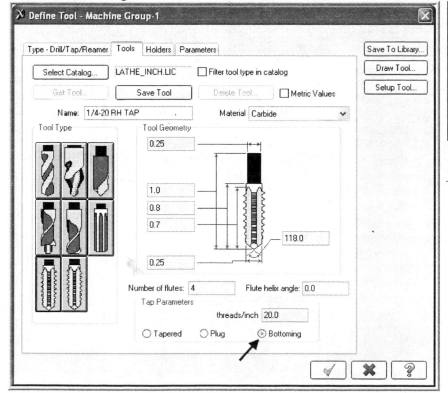

8. Select the **OK** button [✓] to exit the Tools page.

9. Make changes as shown below: The **Spindle Speed** and **Feedrate** are synchronised for a **1/40-20 tap**.

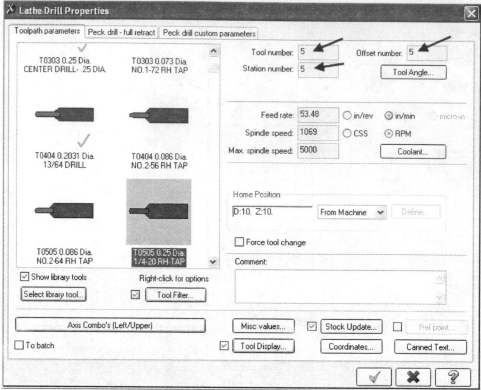

10. Select the **Peck drill – full retract** page and make changes as shown below: This hole will be tapped so **select the Cycle as Tap(G32)** Make changes as shown below:

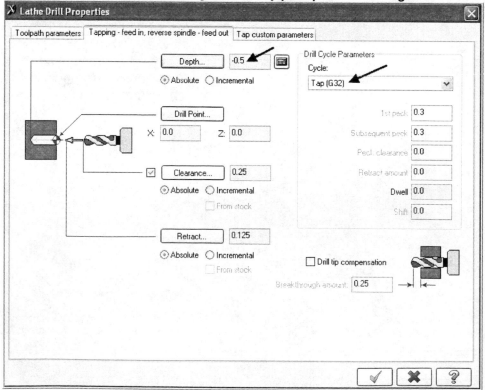

11. Select the **OK** button [✓] to exit Tapping – feed in, reverse spindle – feed out.

TASK 20:
ROUGH THE BORE
➲ In this task you will use a boring tool to rough out the 0.500 diameter bore.

1. From the menu bar select **Toolpaths>Quick>Rough ...**

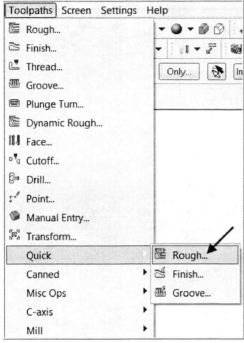

2. In the **Chaining window** Chaining mode is set to Partial by default.
3. Select **Line 1** as the **start** of the Partial chain.

After you have selected the first line ensure that the arrow is pointing towards the part as shown below: If it is not select the reverse button in the Chaining dialog box

4. Then select **Line 2** as the **end** entity in this chain.

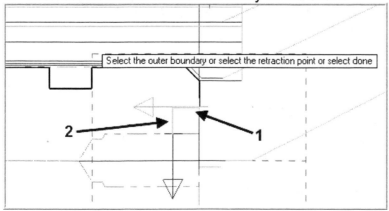

Select the outer boundary or select the retraction point or select done

5. Select the **OK** button to exit the Chaining dialog window.

6. At the **Toolpath parameters** page click on the **Select library tool** button

7. At the top left of this dialog box open up the Select new folder icon ⬆️ to show the library tools list and select **Lathe_Inch.**

8. Select the boring bar **ID ROUGH MIN .1875 – 75 DEGREE.**

Number	Type	Tool Name	Insert Info	Turret
▌ T0101	General Turning	OD ROUGH RIGHT - 80 DEG.	R0.0313	Top
▌ T0202	General Turning	OD ROUGH LEFT - 80 DEG.	R0.0313	Top
▬ T0303	General Turning	ROUGH RIGHT - 80 DEG.	R0.0313	Top
▬ T0404	General Turning	ROUGH LEFT - 80 DEG.	R0.0313 ˙	Top
▌ T1111	General Turning	OD 55 deg Left	R0.0313	Top
▙ T1212	General Turning	OD 55 deg Right	R0.0313	Top
▙ T2121	General Turning	OD FINISH RIGHT - 35 DEG.	R0.0156	Top
▌ T2222	General Turning	OD FINISH LEFT - 35 DEG.	R0.0156	Top
▌ T3131	General Turning	ROUGH FACE RIGHT - 80 DEG.	R0.0313	Top
▌ T3232	General Turning	ROUGH FACE LEFT - 80 DEG.	R0.0313	Top
▬ T7171	Boring bar	ID ROUGH MIN. .1875 DIA. - 75 DEG.	R0.0078	Top
▬ T7272	Boring bar	ID ROUGH MIN. .25 DIA. - 75 DEG.	R0.0078	Top

9. Select the **OK** button ☑️ to exit the selection of this tool.

10. Select the **OK** button for the Duplicate tool numbers warning if it appears.

11. Make any necessary changes as shown below:

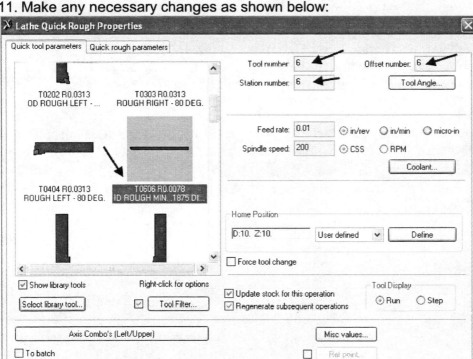

12. Select the **Quick rough parameters** page and make any necessary changes as shown below:

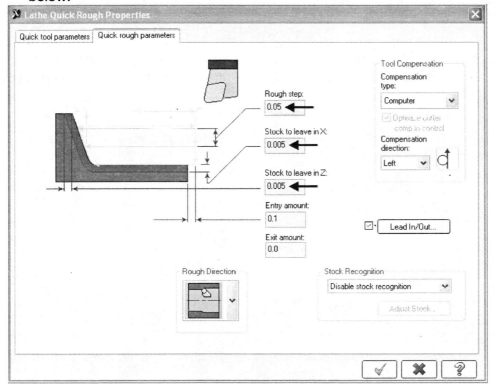

13. Select the **OK** button to exit Rough Parameters.

TASK 21:
FINISH THE BORE

➲ In this task you will use the same boring tool as used for the previous rouging operation.

1. From the menu bar select **Toolpaths> Quick> Finish ...**

2. In the Quick Toolpath parameters page select **Tool #6 a boring tool ID ROUGH MIN .1875 DIA – 75 deg** and make any necessary changes as shown below:

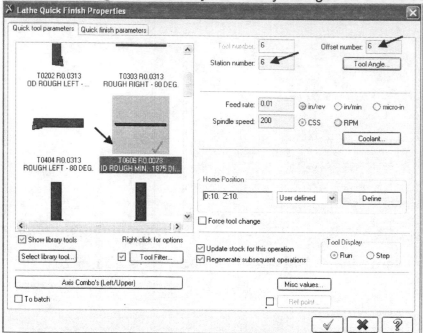

3. Select the **Quick finish parameters** page and make any necessary changes as shown below: Open up the drop down menu for operation and select the operation at the bottom of the list, this is the previous rough boring operation.

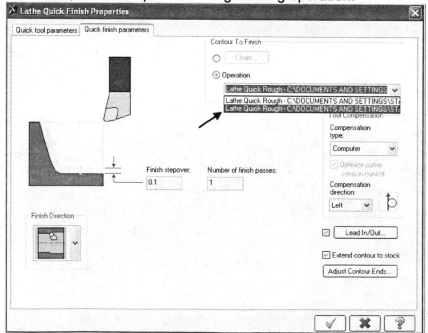

4. Select the **OK** button ✓ to exit Quick finish parameters.

TASK 22:
CUT THE GROOVES

➲ In this task you will use the Lathe Quick Groove toolpath using an **OD Groove Right Width .125**.

1. Select **Alt and T** on the keyboard to hide the toolpath.
2. From the menu bar select **Toolpaths> Quick>Groove ...**

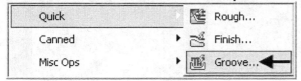

3. The **Groove Options** window appears. Click on the **2 Points** option as shown below:

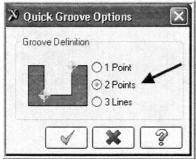

4. Click on **OK** ✓ .
5. Zoom in on the groove areas as shown below:
6. Select **Point 1 and Point 2** for the first groove. Move the cursor over the corner until the visual cue for End point displays and then click on the various points.
7. Then Select **Point 3 and Point 4** for the second groove.

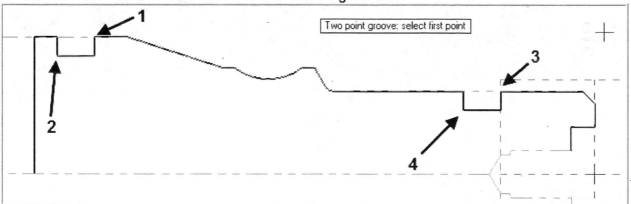

8. Press the **Enter** key when done.

9. Select **OD Groove Right Width .125** tool from the tool list and make any necessary changes as shown below:

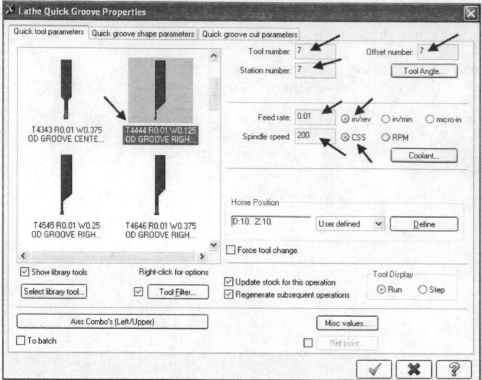

10. Select the **OK** button ✓ to exit as no further changes are required.

TASK 23:
CUT OFF THE PART

➲ In this task you will cut off the part using **OD Groove Right Width .125** the same tool as the previous grooving operation.

1. Fit the image to the screen by clicking on the **Fit** icon as shown below:

2. Then unzoom by clicking on the **Un-zoom Previous / .5** icon as shown below:

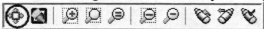

3. From the menu bar select **Toolpaths>Cutoff...**

4. When prompted to **Select cutoff boundary point** pick the end point of the line shown below: Move the cursor over the corner until the visual cue for End point displays and then click on this point.

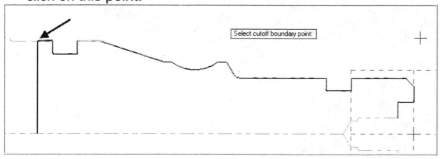

5. Select **OD GROOVE RIGHT WIDTH .125** tool from the tool list and make any necessary changes as shown below:

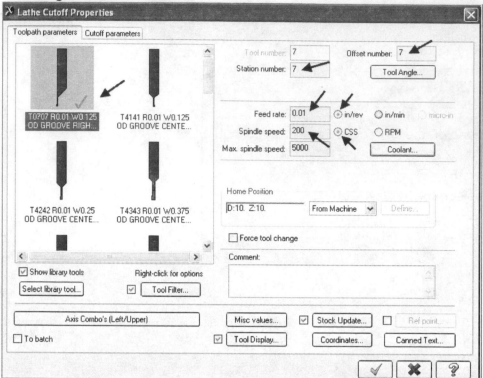

6. Select the **Cutoff parameters** page and make sure the settings are as shown below:

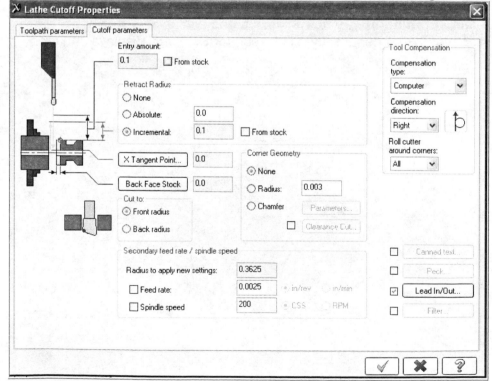

7. Select the **OK** button to exit **Lathe Cutoff parameters.**

TASK 24:
VERIFY THE TOOLPATH

➲ Mastercam's Verify utility allows you to use solid models to simulate the machining of a part. The model created by the verification represents the surface finish, and shows collisions, if any exist.

1. In the Toolpaths Manager pick all the operations to backplot by picking the Select All icon

    .

2. Select the **Verify selected operations** icon shown below:

    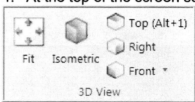

3. **Maximize** the Backplot/Verify window if required.
4. At the top of the screen select the **Isometric** icon and then select **Fit**.

    ```
    ┌─────────────────────────────────────┐
    │  ⊹        ◈      ⬡ Top (Alt+1)      │
    │                                       │
    │                  ⬡ Right             │
    │  Fit   Isometric                     │
    │                  ⬡ Front ▾           │
    │                                       │
    │            3D View                    │
    └─────────────────────────────────────┘
    ```

5. Activate the options shown below in the **Visibility** section of the Home tab. **Initial Stock not** activated.

    ```
    ┌─────────────────────────────────────┐
    │  ☐ Toolpath    ✔ Stock              │
    │  ✔ Tool        ☐ Initial Stock      │
    │  ☐ Workpiece   ✔ Fixtures           │
    │         Visibility                   │
    └─────────────────────────────────────┘
    ```

6. In the lower right corner of the screen now set the run **Speed** to slow by moving the slider bar pointer over to the left as shown below.

    ```
    ┌─────────────────────────────────────┐
    │  Speed:   ⬚─────────────            │
    │          ┴ ┴ ┴ ┴ ┴ ┴ ┴ ┴ ┴ ┴        │
    └─────────────────────────────────────┘
    ```

7. Now select the **Play Simulation** button to review the toolpaths.

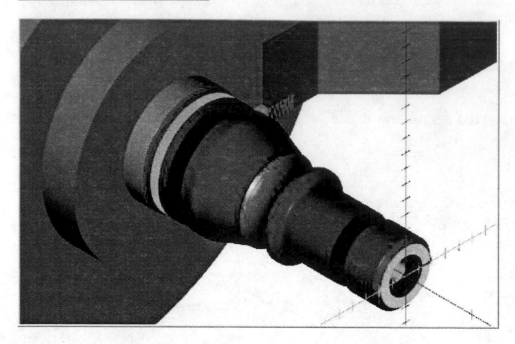

8. Select the **Close** button 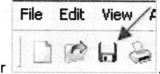 in the top right hand corner to exit Verify.

TASK 25:
SAVE THE UPDATED MASTERCAM FILE

File	Edit	View	/

1. Select the Save icon from the toolbar .

TASK 26:
POST AND CREATE THE CNC CODE FILE

1. Ensure all the operations are selected by picking the **Select All** icon 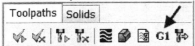 from the Toolpaths manager.

2. Select the **Post selected operations** button from the Toolpaths manager.
➲ **Please Note:** If you cannot see **G1** click on the right pane of the Toolpaths manager window and expand the window to the right.

3. In the Post processing window, make the necessary changes as shown below:

About Post Processing

NC file: Select this option to save the NC file. The file name and extension are stored in the machine group properties for the selected operation. If you are posting operations from different machine groups or Mastercam files, or batch processing, Mastercam will create several files according to the settings for each machine group. **Edit:** When checked, automatically launches the default text editor with the file displayed so that you can review or modify it.

4. Select the OK button [✓] to continue.

5. Ensure the same name as your Mastercam part file name is displayed in the **NC File name** field.
6. Select the **Save** button.
7. The CNC code file opens up in the default editor.

8. Select the [X] in the top right corner to exit the CNC editor.
9. This completes LATHE-LESSON-7.

LATHE-LESSON-7 EXERCISE

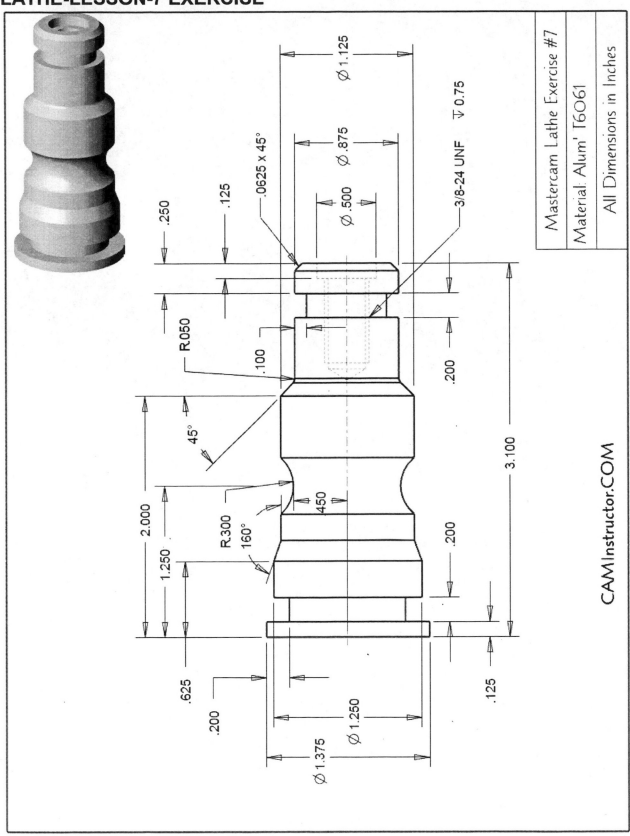

Mastercam Lathe Exercise #7

Material: Alum' T6061

All Dimensions in Inches

Ø 1.125

Ø .875

Ø .500

.0625 x 45°

3/8-24 UNF   ⍌ 0.75

.250

.125

R.050

.100

45°

R.300
160°

450

2.000

1.250

.200

.200

3.100

.625

.200

.125

Ø 1.250

Ø 1.375

CAMInstructor.COM

Mastercam. X⁷

TRAINING

GUIDE

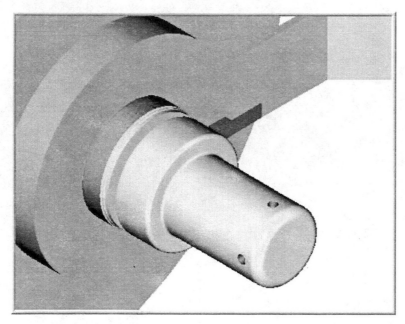

LATHE-LESSON-8

C-AXIS PART

NOTE:
This Lesson is located on the accompanying CD/DVD as a PDF file.
1. Just insert the CD/DVD and click on **Lesson 8** from the Menu screen.
2. Click on **Lesson 8 Instructions (PDF Doc)**.
3. The Lesson can be printed or you can follow the instructions on the computer screen.

camInstructor

camInstructor

Mastercam. X⁷
TRAINING
GUIDE

LATHE-LESSON-9

C-AXIS CROSS CONTOUR

NOTE:

This Lesson is located on the accompanying CD/DVD as a PDF file.

1. Just insert the CD/DVD and click on **Lesson 9** from the Menu screen.
2. Click on **Lesson 9 Instructions (PDF Doc)**.
3. The Lesson can be printed or you can follow the instructions on the computer screen.

camInstructor

camInstructor